CERTIFIED AND DETAINED

The true story of life in an English mental hospital from 1957 to 1963 as seen then through the eyes of a young male student nurse.

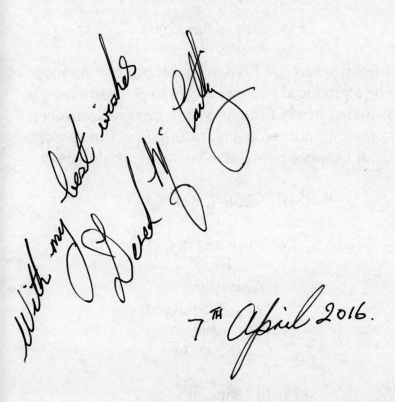

With my best wishes

Derek Mc Carthy

7TH April 2016.

By Derek McCarthy

Published by D & L McCarthy Productions
Email **mrderekmccarthy@talktalk.net**

First edition June 2009.

ISBN 978-0-9562115-0-7

Published and bound
by
ChinaLitho
5F/D 686 Gubei Road,
Shanghai,
China 200336

Email ChinaLitho.cn

This book is dedicated to all of the patients I met in hospital between 1957 and 1963, to my then Principal Tutor John Winkley and my wife Lesley

With special thanks to my proof reader colleague and friend Hugh Chapman

The ill-treated dead cannot speak today of the pain and suffering they endured.

FOREWORD

This book is written to break through the wall of silence that has existed for fifty years about what life was really like in an English Psychiatric Hospital in the late 50's and early 60's. I believe that the grim facts contained in this book can only represent what was then the tip of a very much larger iceberg.

CHAPTER 1.

THE START OF A FIVE YEAR JOURNEY

In January 1957 at the age of 21 after serving 3 years as a professional soldier in the British Army I took early discharge from a 22 year engagement. Following my discharge I briefly joined the ranks of the unemployed until I found a job as a semi skilled factory worker. However the work was dirty, soul destroying and for me a road to nowhere. I hated every moment of it, particularly the grinding monotony of the night shift. As time progressed I became increasingly determined to find something more interesting with prospects, but at the time I hadn't any idea what I was looking for. Hope of escape from the drudgery of factory life came when I saw an advertisement in a local paper for trainee Psychiatric Nurses at St Nicholas Hospital, Gosforth. The advert stated that applicants needed no academic qualifications and that good career prospects were on offer. As I had left school at fifteen with no academic qualifications it sounded as if the job could be right up my street. It was an opportunity too good to miss. Here at last was a job with prospects and one in which I could be doing something useful for a change. So it was with some haste that I put together a letter outlining where I had worked since I left school. However I didn't rate my chances of success very highly. I was almost certain I would receive a reply along the lines "We regret to inform you" etc It was therefore a surprise when about two weeks later a letter addressed to me dropped through the letter box. This in itself was unusual as I never received mail of any kind. This one looked official so I hoped it was a reply from the hospital. I opened the envelope with some trepidation fully expecting to see the dreaded words that confirmed I had been unsuccessful. Then having read the letter twice just to make sure I hadn't misread it the first time, I was delighted to see that it was a request for me to attend for interview. Great news! I could hardly contain my excitement!

The time has passed quickly since I received the letter and today is the day of my interview. So it is with a mixture excitement and anxiety that I have got dressed and ready to catch the bus for a six mile journey to the hospital. It's a lousy day for such a venture, bitterly cold, wet and windy. Upstairs in the bus the windows are all fogged up with condensation so I have cleared a small patch of mist off the glass to peer out as we speed through the town. For most of the journey I am pre-occupied with watching the little dark shapes of rain soaked people scurrying along the streets, some clutching their upturned collars and others with their umbrellas firmly pressed against the wind. It seems no time until the journey is finished and I am suddenly stirred out of my trancelike state by the conductor ringing his bell and shouting "Hospital." I quickly pull myself together and leap down the stairs and jump off the rear platform onto the pavement. Just made it! not a moment to spare!

I see that the hospital main gate with its large sentinel like pillars is only a few feet away from the bus stop and as I pass through its stone portals I see a long drive stretching out ahead of me into the distance. I have never set foot in a psychiatric hospital before and I find it quite daunting particularly on such a miserable dark brooding day. Thankfully the rain has now stopped and as I approach the first rain soaked grey stone building with its dirty curtainless windows it looks very forbidding and mysterious. As I walk past I can imagine that I am being watched from the windows by furtive shadowy figures possibly harbouring malevolent thoughts or intent. My unease is slightly increased by the densely overgrown bushes along the drive. They have dark recesses within them that I feel could conceal a deranged patient waiting to jump out on someone like me. I quickly dismiss these rather fanciful thoughts to concentrate on the immediate prospect of my impending interview.

To create a good impression I have dressed myself as smartly as possible. I don't have an overcoat or a raincoat yet as I can't afford one, so I am just wearing my one and only suit. I wear it on every occasion come rain come shine. I have pressed it so many times that it now shines like silk and it appears as thin as tissue paper from constant cleaning and pressing. The seat of the pants is almost transparent and I dread that they may split if I bend down too suddenly. As I walk up the drive the biting north east wind cuts through the thin fabric like a knife, causing me to shiver and my teeth to chatter uncontrollably. In typical army style I have spit and polished my shoes to a high shine. However what cannot be seen are the soles of the shoes. For weeks now there have been two large holes right through them and as a consequence the bottoms of my socks have been wearing out every two or three days. Also as my unprotected feet have been in direct contact with the ground I have suffered a few painful scrapes. Today for this special occasion I have fashioned two insoles out of cardboard and fitted one into each shoe. However I had not taken into account the possibility of it raining or that the hospital drive might be partly flooded. But unfortunately for me it is flooded and flooded so badly that I can't avoid many of the lake like pools that stretch out in front of me, some spreading across the full width of the road. Inevitably I start to feel the water seeping in as the cardboard in my shoes starts to absorb water like blotting paper. Now every step is accompanied by a loud squelch that can only be avoided by walking on the outside edge of my shoes. Thank God there's no one in sight or they might think I've got bandy legs or that I have just got off a horse. By the time I reach the front entrance to the main building my shoes and socks are water logged and my feet are frozen. Undaunted and as quietly as possible I squelch past the two porters manning the small wooden reception desk and follow the sign that says "To the Psychiatric Training School." As I climb the wooden stairs and enter the school a man comes out of an office and ushers me into a drab empty classroom. He sets me down at a desk and gives me a book and a pen and explains that I have precisely one hour to complete the exam. Fortunately for me I see that completing the task does not require any previous knowledge or any skill in written work. It's called the Progressive Matrix and it involves matching together increasingly difficult patterns. It appears to me at first glance to be a bit of a doddle. When the hour is up the man re-enters the room, removes the book and asks me to wait. I'm slightly disappointed as I have only completed about three quarters of the book but I think I have done fairly well, or at least I hope so. I find it strange that I am the only person here; one explanation could be that people aren't exactly falling over each other to get into this place or maybe it's just that the interviews have been staggered. As I sit patiently waiting for what seems an eternity a very tall distinguished man enters the room and informs me that he is Mr Miller, a nurse administrator who has come to take me on a tour of a few wards. Following him dutifully at a discreet distance we walk up a long corridor past some very strange looking shabby people who are wandering aimlessly about. Then we turn down another corridor to approach a wooden partly glazed door. Mr Miller opens the door with a large key and then ushers me in and closes it behind us. I am immediately confronted with a scene that looks like something from the opera The Rake's Progress. The ward is huge and cavernous and there are dozens of patients milling about, some shouting and others flailing their arms in the air whilst others exhibit the strangest mannerisms that I have ever seen. It is chaotic and I feel isolated and vulnerable despite the fact that there is a large male nurse standing close beside me. Suddenly one patient emerges from the seething throng and marches straight towards me. I am rooted to the spot. I brace myself as it appears as if he is going to walk straight through me but then suddenly he stops just a foot away. His impassive face is uncomfortably close to mine as he stares directly at me with cold steel blue watery eyes. His mouth is open and from between his yellow and brown teeth his rancid breath wafts across my face. He stands there motionless and glares at me with a fixed expression like that of hate or suspicion. I am totally unnerved and don't know whether to smile or move or what. So I don't move a muscle but just stare back with what I hope is a pleasant or non-threatening expression. Suddenly he spins quickly around and I just manage not to jump with fright. He then marches back into the milling throng and is lost from sight. Thank God for that! I breathe a sigh of relief. As I regain my composure Mr Miller says we will leave now and I cannot get back through the door quickly enough. Outside in the corridor Mr Miller turns to me and says blandly "You see it's just like home" He must be joking or being sarcastic it's nothing like my home, not in a million years it's not. The rest of the tour is very interesting but thankfully uneventful. As I say goodbye to Mr Miller he says they will be in touch. Walking back down the drive I instinctively know that despite my first frightening experience I would love to do this type of job. All I can hope for now is that I have been successful in my application.

Three months have now passed and unbelievably I have been successful and got the job. It's 1958 and it's my first year as a student nurse. I have spent the first six weeks in the training school in a class of 15 male and female students. I was right when I thought I would love this work. It's even way beyond my expectations. It's just what I have always wanted, its exciting, interesting, variable and very worthwhile. I cannot believe my luck. I have been issued with ten white coats and a handful of white uniform buttons, a bunch of keys and a hospital dark blue serge suit with two pairs of trousers. I am now the proud owner of two suits and a good pair of shoes, which is more than I have ever had before.

Today is my first day on the wards and I have been allocated to the very ward where I had my first frightening experience. At 7.30 am as I walk onto the ward for the first time I am greeted by a very large charge nurse who looks in his fifties. He smiles broadly and introduces himself as Tommy Fluke. Still smiling he asks me if I have had breakfast and when I answer no he ushers me into a narrow cupboard stacked with linen and shuts the door behind me. A few minutes later he returns with a steaming mug of tea and a pile of scrambled egg sandwiches. This is certainly royal treatment for a mere student nurse on his first day on duty. When I finish eating he takes me on a tour of the ward, making comments as we go and pointing out various patients who have just got out of bed. The wards much quieter than when I saw it last but maybe that's partly due to it being very early in the morning, my being more familiar with the surroundings and generally feeling more confident. I'm sure I can cope now even if it hots up later in the day. As the charge nurse and I walk through the day room I notice a tiny old man who is obviously blind feeling his way cautiously around one of the dining room tables. As we pass him Mr Fluke shouts impatiently "Get in there you old bugger" and gives him a resounding smack across the back of his head. The old man is sent reeling across the room and his momentum is only brought to a halt by colliding with the wall. He tries unsuccessfully to clutch onto something but there is nothing there for him to get a grip on. Finally he manages to steady himself and feel his way around the door post and into the bathroom. Without a further word the charge nurse takes me onto the ward veranda. As we enter he turns to me and says "What's a nice young feller like you doing coming to work in a place like this. Don't you know if you live amongst shit you become shit" I'm lost for words so I don't reply and just shrug my shoulders. The force and conviction of his words combined with the slapping of the little blind man make me realise that he means every word. Having just been in school being taught how to treat patients with care and dignity this is the last thing I expected to see or hear from a nurse in charge of a ward.

Two weeks have now gone by and despite the shocking introduction to the ward I have enjoyed the work even though it has been an unending slog of cleaning, bumping floors, bathing patients, serving meals and giving endless enemas.

The patients here are real characters but very deteriorated in their habits. Some will eat the potted plants and sometimes even the stones in the soil. The early mornings are the worst, with up to a dozen badly soiled beds to change, it's a real clothes peg on the nose job. Yesterday when I was giving a patient an enema I retrieved several lengths of plastic mattress cover from his rear end. It appeared that he had torn strips off the cover and eaten them, It's a miracle the lengths of plastic didn't cause an internal blockage.

My time on this my first ward has now come to an end. The six weeks have flown past. During this time I have never witnessed Mr Fluke strike another patient or rough handle any of them. I cannot think of an explanation why he slapped the defenceless little blind man. Maybe it was a single aberration, maybe his gastritis was playing him up! I will never know. Sure, at times he was angry and sometimes he would shout at patients but most of the time he was very kind, fair and good humoured towards them. He has also been particularly good to me and taught me a lot.

Several months have passed since I left Tommy Fluke's ward and I have now worked on several other wards and with a considerable number of staff. On reflection during my time in the army I met some very colourful characters and faced some unusual and tough situations but I have discovered that working in a psychiatric hospital made them all pale into insignificance. Before becoming a student here I had no previous experience of people who were mentally ill but I guessed the work would be unusual and possibly bizarre but not quite as unusual and bizarre as I have now found out. In the time I have worked here it has become clear that there are some of the strangest people you would ever wish, or more likely not wish to meet. There are a few people here who are fantasists with a tenuous grip on reality, colourful homosexuals, psychopaths, petty thieves, sadists, pathological liars and these are just some of the staff. There are also a small number of people called managers who are under the illusion that they are in charge and controlling the situation. At the bottom of the ladder, if they are on the ladder at all, are third class citizens called patients, many of whom have been in hospital for many years. They suffer from a number of distressing and debilitating illnesses such as schizophrenia, general paralysis of the insane caused by untreated syphilis, severe epilepsy, psychopathic disorders, depression, brain injuries, Huntington's Chorea, Parkinson's Disease and mental deficiency. Additionally some have been robbed of the last vestiges of their personality and become almost automatons. They have been reduced to this state by crude frontal lobe brain surgery, less affected are those who have been subjected to huge doses of electro-convulsive therapy, (ECT). some of which has been administered in the past without a general anaesthetic or muscular relaxant. These debilitating illnesses and their so called treatments are more than sufficient for a patient to cope with but unfortunately they also have had to live in this hospital effectively as prisoners for an undefined period of time in what is a soulless and bleak environment under the regimented control of white coated doctors and nurses.

At present I am hoping against hope that I won't be placed on yet another long stay or geriatric ward. What I find difficult to understand is that I came here to look after people who have problems in their heads yet for the past few months I have been at the other end dealing with their waste products.

Once again I make my way down the corridor to where the duty lists are posted. As I arrive there is a crowd around the notice board and it looks like a mini rugby scrum. After waiting patiently for a gap to occur in the throng I gradually push my way to the front past several charge nurses. Charge Nurses are particularly interested to see where they are being placed. Long serving members of staff have told me previously that some Charge Nurses can almost double their salary if they are placed in charge of a ward containing long stay dependent institutionalised patients. They achieve the additional perks by stealing patient's pocket and comfort money and by misappropriating goods and money brought in by patients relatives. Some nurses say that if something is not screwed down here it will walk out. Others describe these thefts as part of the extended loan system, a loan never to be repaid!

I myself have seen the extent of this pilfering on those wards I have previously worked on and I have been to the homes of several nurses where the towels, sheets, blankets and pillow cases all have the hospital stamp on them. Craning my neck I manage to locate my name on the change lists and see that I have been allocated to yet another geriatric ward. Oh well I suppose working on another one won't be so bad; at least they all vary, and I will be working with different patients and different staff. One ward I don't want to be allocated to yet is Ward 20. This ward is known as the Refractory Ward. It's a locked facility that holds the most seriously ill and disturbed patients. I have heard many gruelling tales about this ward from fellow students and staff nurses. However, knowing the tendencies of some of them to exaggerate or even fabricate stories I think some maybe fanciful or even untrue. One nurse told me that he got involved in a fight with a patient during visiting time. He said the patient's father had held him from behind while the patient knocked his two front teeth out. I have a suspicion that some of the stories like these may contain elements of truth as my cousin Michael McComish has been a patient on this ward for many years, ever since he was invalided out of the army. My 70year old grandmother who visits him regularly has told members of the family that he is often covered in bruises and that on several occasions he has had black and swollen eyes. Michael's explanation is that the staff have hit him, which at the time I instinctively believed. I have also heard that the ward charge nurse called Bob is said to run the ward with a rod of iron. He is also the hospitals Union Branch Secretary and, more importantly, the National President of the Confederation of Health Service Employees (COHSE) He is known throughout the hospital to be a hard man in every respect. Some nurses and managers are said to fear him, others hold him in awe whilst a few, mainly Union activists appear almost to hero-worship him. As the branch secretary in what is almost a closed shop he is said to be a force to be reckoned with. I have also heard that he is a master of the double standard, preaching about good care from various national union platforms whilst ruthlessly pursuing his own personal ambitions and blocking all progressive reforms that might release the Unions iron grip on staff. However despite the fact that he is in a position of power he does not appear to have any modern qualifications. I have been informed that he holds the qualification of RMPA; that stands for the rather grandiose title of the Royal Medico-Psychological Association. A form of training started in 1890 for asylum attendants. Initially it was a two-year training course that was later extended to three years. The last examinations were held around 1949. I think he may be similar in character to some of the other dinosaurs I have met here from an era when nurses in these hospitals were little more than jailers.

I have now completed my first year of training and I have worked on a number of wards. Some of the time the work has been most enjoyable. Many of the staff I have worked with were very good and I have got to know many more patients and learned a lot about their illnesses. My best experience was without doubt in the Psychiatric Training School (PTS) This was the first time I had met my female student nursing colleagues. In keeping with a number of my fellow male students I had found two of them particularly attractive. They were completely contrasting in looks, one was very blonde and Nordic looking with a quiet personality while the other was typically Irish with black hair and blue eyes and a flamboyant personality. The competition from some of my pals for their attention was quite fierce but in the long run I won through with the dark one and we started dating. The whole time spent in school was exhilarating and in many ways was in marked contrast with working in the wards. For here in school our senior tutor John Winkley confirmed by his teaching our innate beliefs about how patients should really be treated whilst in some wards I learned what not to do by the negative and cruel things I witnessed.

At the end of my time in school my girlfriend and I decided to get married and I have reluctantly made up my mind to leave the hospital to be enable us to get a mortgage. This means that I will have to discontinue training and go back into factory work which I hated but where I will get a salary three times higher than I am getting as a student. It was therefore with great regret that I left the hospital and returned to working as a universal miller in a marine turbine factory.

The following year in the factory was very hard, working alternately two weeks on nights and two weeks on days. The work was dirty, noisy, and monotonous,. but the pay was good and it did enable us to buy two old terrace flats one of which had a sitting tenant. With the extra income coming in from the leased flat we decided that we could manage financially on lower pay, although it would be a struggle. So once again I applied to the hospital to become a student nurse and was thrilled and rather surprised that I was accepted for a second time. I recommenced training in February 1959. Initially I thought that I would be credited for the original year in training but unfortunately this was not to be. I was told that I would have to start my training again and do another three years. The reason for this was that a new Mental Health Act had been introduced in 1959 and as a consequence the training syllabus had been completely changed.

I have now got over the disappointment of having to start again and work for another three years and I am pleased to be back. I have just completed working on another three wards, the first two were for geriatrics and the third was a long stay ward for those with chronic mental illnesses. It was the same ward on which I had started my initial training, but Tommy Fluke had moved on and his place had been taken by another charge nurse who rarely came out of his office and hardly ever spoke. He used to communicate with me by thrusting notes in my hand, often containing a list of ten or more patients to whom single handed I had to give liquid soap enemas. This task was akin to the most vile type of mud wrestling you can imagine. It involved a procedure that demanded the dexterity of a juggler, a skill in wrestling and the nose and stomach of a sewage worker. For the patient it involves a total loss of dignity and the most excruciating griping pain.

The procedure is to lie the patient naked on a bed that is covered with a thick red rubber sheet. Once the patient is lying in position you have to hold him down with your left elbow while clutching with that hand a large funnel attached to a lengthy rubber tube. With your right hand you insert the tube up his rectum. You then have to quickly grab a large jug of thick liquid green soap with the same hand and pour the solution into the funnel whilst managing to keep the struggling patient on the bed and at the same time trying to keep the tube from coming out and spilling its contents on the patient and the bed. I will not describe the end product of this procedure as its too nauseating to describe. Afterwards eating egg sandwiches at breakfast time is definitely a no, no with hands smelling like mine. It's an extremely undignified experience for the patient and also a procedure that most nurses would wish to avoid.

This week I have seen some disposable enemas and applicators in the ward stock cupboard. The charge nurse has agreed that I can use them but has informed me that they are not as effective as the green liquid soap and that they are expensive.

Armed with several of these enema packs I get six patients to follow me into the toilets. In turn I place each one in a separate toilet and as each drops his trousers I go from one cubicle to the next and administer the enema. In less than five minutes I have completed the task and shut all of the cubicle doors. What a difference, there is no messy aftermath, nothing to dispose of and almost completed privacy and very little loss of dignity for the patient. Another plus is that I have saved over two hours of work and protected myself from contamination.

We have been forewarned of an impending visit by Enoch Powell the Minister of Health and so we have embarked on cleaning everything in sight,. windows, floors, brasses etc. It's the first time the hospital has been visited by a Minister of Health and everything is now ready. It's the morning of this momentous event and the ward is spick and span and the patients are all in their new suits. I am in my sparkling white coat and I have been given the job of playing snooker with two of the more able patients. They know which end of the snooker cue to use but as far as the rules of the game are concerned they don't appear to have a clue. We are in the midst of a rather confused game when the main ward door bursts open and in pour Enoch Powell and his entourage of senior hospital doctors, managers and health officials. With head down he strides quickly through the day room looking neither to the left or the right. Not even a glance at the patients, not a word to the staff and most importantly not a word to me. What an opportunity he missed! They quickly disappear through the door into the dormitory and are then gone. I think to myself is that it, not even a word or a glance! All that work for nowt! What a waste of time. It is my first experience of a ministerial visit and I am far from being impressed. It's yet another negative lesson amongst a number of negative lesson I have learned in this place. However by putting all of the positive and negative lessons together helps me to more fully understand what makes the entire hospital tick and to know why it is so difficult to move the institution forward.

I have two days left to work on this ward and I have again been down to see the change list. I have been allocated to the Refractory Ward, the dreaded Ward 20. The difference now is that I feel I have had sufficient experience to be fairly confident that I can face this new challenge.

CHAPTER 2.

THE REFRACTORY WARD

It's with a mixture of excitement, anxiety and foreboding that at 6.30am on my first 14 hour shift I approach Ward 20 at the bottom of the corridor, bedecked in my pristine white coat and flourishing my bunch of keys that are the outward symbols of my authority. I turn my key in the lock and slowly climb the stone steps that lead up to the second locked ward door. As I approach the door I can hear some muffled banging and shouting which increases my apprehension. Once inside the ward the shouting and banging grows louder, reverberating towards me down the long corridor. My first impression is the same as that which I have formed on many of my previous wards. Drab half wood panelled walls, old cream paint, dark parquet block floors and the smell of Mansion Polish. As I walk purposefully down the corridor towards the day room I see on my left a number of locked security bedrooms. As I pass I see some gruesome and grimacing faces of patients pressed hard against the doors wired security glass. Some of the patients momentarily stop banging their fists on the doors, possibly anticipating that I may let them out, while others are possibly curious about the new face in a white coat entering their domain. One of these patients I recognise instantly as my cousin Michael but even in the brief second of passing I am aware that it is not the happy go lucky Michael that I knew many years ago.

As I enter the Day Room the charge nurse is coming out of the toilet area. I dutifully tell him my name and explain that I am a newly allocated student. I had expected that Bob Vickerstaff would be in charge but he is obviously not on duty today. The replacement charge nurse ushers me into the dormitory which is full of patients scurrying around and a number of white-coated nurses. I follow him up the lines of beds and he introduces me to one of the staff nurses. He then turns to me and says, "He will show you the ropes." and walks off. My new found colleague and I make a few beds together then he tells me to follow him to get patients out of the locked side rooms.

As we approach the rooms I notice bundles of crumpled clothes on the floor piled outside each door. As I unlock and open the first door the stench of stale urine hits me. The patient is sitting on the edge of his bed; he has apparently poured the contents of his chamber pot over his head, bed and floor. In an indentation in the mattress nestles a stagnant pool of dark brown urine with a mound of excreta in the middle. The smell of ammonia is almost overpowering as he scurries past me in his soaking nightshirt, grabbing his clothes from the floor outside the door as he goes. I unlock the wood window security shutters and reach to open the narrow vent at the bottom of the window to let some fresh air into the room. Cleaning the mess up is no problem as I have previously been on geriatric wards where this amount of urine and excrement is insignificant. On those wards in the morning you can face up to 10 or 20 beds full of urine and faeces. I muse to myself that I should be given a golden shovel award as since I have been in this hospital I have dealt with enough human excreta to fertilize all of the rose gardens of England.

In the next room I find a small, thin elderly man curled up in his bed. I ask him politely to get up and shake him by his shoulder, there is no response, I shake him again but still I get no response. I see from the coal scratches on his forehead, nose and hands that he is an ex- miner. Seeing that my shaking and requests are getting nowhere I decide to get assistance. No sooner has the thought entered my head than the charge nurse comes barging into the room almost as if he had anticipated a problem. He grabs the old man by the scruff of the neck and drags him out of bed, shouting as he does "Out, you lazy old bastard," When the patient makes no response he roughly twists his hand in the back of the patient's nightshirt and pulls him out of bed along the floor and out of the room. I follow them into the corridor to see the patient being dragged into the day room with his nightshirt riding up around his back and his spindly legs and heels trailing along the wooden block floor. The patient is then flung into a large leather chair as I dutifully stand behind with his clothes and shoes. The charge nurse takes them from me and thrusts them towards the patient "Get your fucking clothes on." There is no response. Then out of the blue comes an explosion of anger, of the type I have seen so many times before. Obviously still getting no response is the final straw. The charge nurse then brings his heavy booted foot hard down across the unprotected bare feet of the patient. This time the response is immediate, the patient lets out a cry of pain and bends forward to clutch his feet. I sense it's not over yet as the charge nurse grabs the patient by the hair pulling him arched over the back of the chair. He then sinks a very heavy punch into the pit of the old mans stomach. The patient jack-knifes forward in agony. At this point the charge nurse turns towards me and says simply "See to him" and strides off apparently unconcerned. This is one of many scenes that I have previously witnessed where violence erupts out of nowhere, with little or no provocation, and ends just as quickly, almost as if it has never happened. I am left to see to the patient and it takes me several minutes to get him dressed as I have to struggle to get each item of clothing on. He hardly seems aware of what I am trying to do.

During the afternoon I decide to speak to my cousin Michael who up until now has shown no sign of recognising me. I see he is pacing the day room and as I approach he suddenly stops and looks straight at me with an unintelligible grin on his face. Slightly unnerved I feel prompted to speak. "Hello Michael do you remember me?" He doesn't reply but continues to look at me, I press him further "Remember me. I used to live with you at Suttons Dwellings." His grin becomes even more weird. "Yes you're my granny." he replies. He is slightly off beam, I am sure I don't look like his grandmother but he has apparently made some connection between us as for a short period we both lived with our grandmother in a ground floor flat in a tenement building. He then appears to lose interest and walks quickly away. I decide to leave it at that as I have been told he can be very aggressive. I decide to try to engage him more meaningfully later.

The following four days have been at the beck and call of the charge nurse and staff nurses in an endless routine of menial domestic chores, bathing and shaving patients, scrubbing and polishing floors, cleaning windows and making endless cups of tea. Relief comes four times a day, the first is when the staff have breakfast , the second is tea break in the morning, the third is during the unofficial staff rest time after lunch and the fourth during the afternoon tea break. We also get a little respite when we count patients out into the airing courts for an hour's exercise. In the exercise court one of my usual allocated tasks is to stand at one corner of the high walled court to watch patients shuffling round the perimeter path in an endless circle. The airing court has a nine foot wall around it with a three foot ditch on the inside running around the perimeter. Occasionally a member of staff will bring a football out and some patients will make a half-hearted attempt to kick the ball and then quickly lose interest. Today it is cold with drizzling rain but despite this a member of staff has brought a leather football out and staff are enjoying themselves taking pot shots at unsuspecting patients, preferably in the hope of hitting them on the back or even better the head. There are several near misses then one patient gets hit on the legs and another on the back, at which point a cheer goes up from the staff. Albert the obsessional is less fortunate, he takes a resounding hit on the back of his head with the heavy wet leather ball. There is laughter and a louder cheer from the staff as Albert scurries away out of range.

During these first few days on the ward what I have enjoyed most is getting to know the patients many of whom have very odd personalities and strange patterns of behaviour. There is Psyche who continually punches himself in the face. Jimmy the masochist who enjoys inflicting pain on himself. Tommy Myers an ex Chindit, captured by the Japanese; his penchant is breaking windows, usually as many as he can before staff stop him. Freddy

McGurn a good Roman Catholic boy with schizophrenia who attends Mass every Sunday, Albert the ward runner or trusty who has an obsessional compulsive disorder, Patrick a huge but dim Irishman and my cousin Michael McComish. There are many others whose personalities and activities I now know but whose names I have yet to get fixed in my mind.

I have now also got to know the layout of the ward and its security features and systems. The general appearance of the ward is very similar to the wards I have worked on previously. It's a bleak place, the general impression is that of a barrack room with half panelled dark wood walls and parquet floors. The windows are small paned and Georgian in style with restricted sash openings at the top and bottom. The glass panes are small, small enough to put your fist through but fortunately not your head. All of the doors and cupboards are permanently locked and can only be opened by the staff's personal master key. In the corridor there are five locked patient security rooms that have heavy wooden shutters at the windows and one padded cell in the corner of the day room. The dark oak furniture is very robust and of plain basic design with heavy dark brown leather covering. The heating of the ward is minimal which adds significantly to the Spartan environment. The toilets, or backs as they are called, are securely locked and freezing cold even on a reasonably warm day; not the sort of place to encourage you to maintain good hygiene. There are two large cast iron baths standing side by side, offering no privacy as there is not a curtain between them. The bath taps can be removed to prevent incidents of drowning or scalding. All the pipes in the toilets and the flushing mechanisms are boxed in to prevent patients from hanging themselves.

Any patient who is suicidal is placed on the Red Card regime. Red cards identify all of the known self harm risks to the patient and every member of staff must sign the card to confirm that they are aware of the risk and accepts personal responsibility for keeping the patient under constant observation.

On my fourth day I finish my run of shifts, 14 hours on the first day followed by three 12-hour days. During my time on the ward I have suffered from a number of tension headaches caused by having to be constantly on my guard against fights between patients and others breaking windows, having to participated in restraining patients, dealing with patients during epileptic fits and preventing those intent on self-harm. I now feel shattered, it has been an interesting and challenging four days but I now have the satisfaction of knowing that I can cope on this the most difficult ward in the hospital. I'm looking forward to the luxury of three full days off; well not exactly off but three days working at my part time job in a sheet metal and woodwork factory. This additional part time work helps me to supplement my meagre weekly wage of six pounds ten shillings.

Time has passed quickly I am back on duty and my three days off seem to have flown by. As I wearily enter the ward at 6.30 am. I notice as I pass the open office door that Bob the charge nurse is at his desk, obviously back from holiday. At staff breakfast time I sit opposite him and study him intently. I estimate that he is in his mid forties, smaller than me about 5ft 8 inches of slim but compact athletic build. His complexion is sallow. He has high cheekbones and a well defined mouth with a perfect set of ivory coloured teeth. His eyes are steel grey, cold and penetrating. His silver grey hair is slightly greased and sleeked straight back. The one brief smile he allows himself during breakfast makes him appear more menacing than friendly, rather like a rhesus sardonicus grimace. His voice is monotone and gravelly. Overall his appearance is immaculate. I also note the deference shown to him by the staff nurses around the table. during the break.

The next two days have been relatively quiet but one particular situation caught my attention. It's the ward routine to only open the toilets for about ten minutes every two or three hours throughout the day. Patients requesting to go to the toilet outside this time frame are usually refused and presumably hold on until they are opened. When I am in the large day room I have noticed that patients keep wandering out of my line of sight into the dining room. I have then heard the sash windows being opened and closed. After a few moments the patients come back into the dayroom. My curiosity aroused I decide to quietly follow the next patient at a discreet distance. I don't have to wait long before I notice that Albert the obsessional is heading out of the day room. For the last half hour he had been becoming more and more fidgety in his chair. I let him get a few paces ahead and quietly follow behind him. When I get to the glass partition that separates the dining room from the day room I stop this side and peer round it. Albert has his back to me facing the bay window. Intrigued I noticed that he has one of his shoes in his hand and is sliding the window up with the other. He then unbuttons his trousers and urinates into his shoe before deftly pouring the contents out of the upstairs window. I hope no unsuspecting person is walking below. He then closes the window and slips his shoe back on as I duck behind the partition and move back quickly into the day room. I think that I am the only member of staff who has observed this bizarre but essential practice and I now know why patient's shoes and socks smell so bad.

It's day three I have been given the early morning job of supervising the patient's washing and shaving in the toilet area. I have handed out four locked safety razors and Jimmy the masochist is directly standing in front of me shaving in the mirror. Suddenly a fist flies past my face and lands squarely on Jimmies jaw knocking him sideways. He drops the razor, recovers his balance and with a shout goes after his assailant Michael McComish. I can hear further shouting coming from the day room as a fight ensues. I am mystified by this sudden apparently unprovoked attack. Maybe it is just Michael kicking off for no reason or maybe he is settling an old score. When I see them next they are both reeking of paraldehyde; someone has obviously given them a liberal dose of this vile tasting oral tranquiliser. It has a very strong pungent smell on the breath but some patients love it and can knock back 2 ounces of the vile tasting liquid like a Scotsman taking a dram of his favourite whisky.

As dinnertime approaches I notice that Tommy Myers is getting very worked up, pacing back and forwards, muttering with his arms clutched close to his sides. I have been told that Tommy was in the Chindits, the largest group of Special Forces in action during the 2nd World War and that he was taken prisoner by the Japanese. The Chindits were led by Major General Orde Wingate and lived and fought deep behind the Japanese lines in the jungles of Northern Burma. They fought two major battles in 1943 and 1944 and took suffered up to 50%

casualties. In their first battle 944 were killed, 2434 were wounded and 452 were posted missing. During their expeditions behind Japanese lines the seriously ill or wounded were shot by their own men rather than being left to fall into Japanese hands. Half of those unfortunate enough to be captured died in captivity. They were either murdered by the Japanese or died of ill treatment, starvation and disease. During captivity Tommy was brutalised until his mind was almost totally destroyed. On his return to Britain there was no homecoming victory parade for him, no return to the welcoming arms of his family. No return to the promised "Land fit for Heroes." There was just a place in a refractory ward in a mental hospital with further brutality inflicted on him by some of his fellow countrymen. Tommy is now a pathetic sight; he is over 6 foot tall and dressed in the usual patient garb, a shabby misshapen suite, with trouser bottoms about 6 inches above his skinny ankles. His long sallow clown like face and uneven badly stained teeth and his gangly emaciated body is reminiscent of the wartime pictures of people in concentration camps. He walks with his hands tightly to his sides, clutching his trouser. When he is spoken to he calls you "Your extreme holiness" and often if he thinks you are unhappy with him he will get on his knees and prostrate himself in front of you with his arms outstretched along the floor, just as he may have been forced to do by his brutal Japanese guards. I have been told that when stress becomes too much for him he will break windows to relieve the tension.

After lunch I notice that Tommy is becoming more and more agitated only a few yards away from where the charge nurse is sitting reading the paper. I already know that this is not a good time for patients to kick off and cause a disturbance because this time after lunch is the unofficial staff rest time. Every patient is expected to remain seated while the staff read the papers or chat together over a cup of tea. Tommy's increasing agitation is being steadfastly ignored by all the staff until suddenly there is a loud bang, then another and yet another, three windows gone. Bob leaps from his chair with a "fuck you," he drags Tommy away from the windows and rams him up against the wall. He then crosses his hands and slides them inside the collar of Tommy jacket. He then quickly jerks his hands forward and turns his wrists inwards towards the side of Tommy's neck. Tommy's face starts to turn blue and then purple as he blacks out and slumps to the floor. He is then dragged away along the floor by the charge-nurse and staff nurse to be medicated in the dormitory. I have heard about the practice of blacking out patients from Jimmy Seatory a student who was in my original class but who is now a year ahead of me in training. He was on this ward before me and has described to me the types of brutality he has seen. He's given a name to every sadistic method used.

They come under his general description of "Thump Therapy." This particular practice he calls The Warder's Lock. It involves pulling the neck muscles away from the carotid arteries and then compressing them with an inward turn of the wrists. This shuts off the blood supply to the brain, causing the patient to blackout without the danger of obstructing their airway and causing asphyxiation. Jimmy uses various neologisms to describe many other cruel practices, such as "The Drops". "The "TTT" (the terrible towel treatment.) "The Water Works" and The Zigzag" etc. As yet I haven't seen any member of staff use these practices but from what I have seen so far I have little doubt that I will in due course.

Many times I have heard people say this is a civilised country and that the National Health Service is the best in the world. I disagree on both counts, the system here is far from civilised and if this is the best care system in the world God help the rest.

The afternoon has come quickly and we are out in the airing court again. The weather is still cold but fine and we have taken a football with us. We count the patients out one by one. Michael McComish springs to life when the ball is passed to him and he keeps the ball in the air by first kicking and then heading it. He is quite skilled at this and I have watched him do this many times when we were young boys living together. As the patients trudge past me I feel quite sad as I notice again how shabby and dejected they all look. Most of their trousers are at half-mast and the shoulder pads of their jackets are lumpy and misshapen. The state of the patient's suits is due to the fact that they are not dry-cleaned but washed in almost boiling water. After two or three such launderings even a new suit quickly becomes shrunk and shapeless. I also notice how many of the patient's shoes are without laces while others are trodden down at the back through constantly being taken on and off with the laces still fastened. One patient is trying the handle of the door leading out into the hospital grounds in the vain hope that it will be unlocked. A nurse shouts to him to "Pack it in". A small group of patients sit on the grass with their coats over their bowed heads. Who knows what they are thinking about, if in fact they are thinking about anything. God only knows! Over the years how many times have they walked round these courts. How many times have they thought about being separated from their families. No wonder they are dejected and institutionalised. Under these circumstance any normal person would be, certainly I would. After an hour of this mind numbing boredom we count all the patients back in again and get ready for tea.

Teatime has passed without incident and we all settle down to watch TV. The one thing that has dramatically improved the lives of patients in here is the introduction of TV to the wards. It has brought the wide outside world into the closed world of the mad house. Above all it has brought laughter and entertainment into the patient's lives, commodities that are in very short supply here. So far I have never heard a patient crack a joke or smile with delight or happiness.

Over the last two weeks I have got to know the names and personalities of some of the staff but it's strange, I come on duty, go through a seemingly endless routine over four 12 hour days but never really get to know anyone in any real depth. Maybe it's me or possibly it's because I am just a student and of no real consequence and I will be moving on to another ward in a few weeks time. I have noticed that there is not much real loyalty here either. For example one of the staff nurses has a flirtatious wife with a very high sex drive that is apparently satisfied outside her marriage. Several of the trained staff here openly boast of having had sex with her but when her staff nurse husband is on the ward they act as if they are his best pals. Recently I was at a party and unfortunately Bob the charge nurse was there too. It's bad enough having to work with him but being with him at a social occasion is even worse. However most of the evening I managed to avoid him.

On a few occasions at lunch time I meet two of my student pals, David and Alan and we go for a walk around the grounds. It's our opportunity to compare notes about what we have seen and heard since we last met. From these brief talks it is clear to the three of us that there are endemic levels of cruelty, repression and neglect on many wards throughout the male side of the hospital. It's interesting that two of my three friends have strong religious convictions. David intends to go into the ministry and Alan is a Jehovah's Witness. I too have a strong religious background first as an evangelical in a breakaway sect of the Plymouth Brethren and later as a Roman Catholic. However I have become a convinced agnostic through what I like to believe is a process of logical thinking, although in common with my pals I still adhere to the value system laid down by the man called Christ, but not the church. Our only disagreement is on the divinity bit. I must be the only agnostic who has been christened four times, once a baby in a C of E church, once by total immersion in an evangelical church and twice as a Roman Catholic. All of my pals know that much of what we see in the hospital is very wrong but none of us has ever even tentatively suggested that we should make a stand together to complain either to the managers or our tutors.

At present the chances of improving the patient's lives here seems light years away. Two major things stopping progress are the Union and the system for promoting staff. Once qualified promotion here is not on merit, it is literally "dead men's shoes." Hardly any staff have moved from here to other hospitals mainly because they too operate the same system for promotion. So it is just a matter of waiting your turn, keeping your nose clean and hey presto you get promoted at around 40 or 50. Then you just soldier on to retirement. Many of the staff here came from the armed forces after the Second World War or from the heavy northern industries such as the iron or steel works or the coal mines. Many were picked for their height and brawn rather than their brain or because they were good at football or cricket or played a musical instrument. Winning sporting events against another hospital is considered a high achievement and one to be relished. A place on the hospital band is also a prestigious position. The working hours have always been long and the pay poor but there are many other perks. It's a job for life and superannuated too. However, people looking for work are not queuing up to get in here and all the patients who still have their marbles just want to get out as soon as possible. Some things here are a bit of a laugh for instance in 1959 the Government brought in a new Mental Health Act and in response the medical staff re-graded most of the patients to informal/voluntary status. Very few of the patients were informed of the change or if they had been most of them wouldn't have understood the implications of what they were being told and those that could understand would have been detained again if they had tried to leg it. I am sure it looks very good on the books to be able to demonstrate that 90% of the patients are here on an informal basis and can supposedly leave if they wish.

Segregation is another phenomenon here, both for staff and patients. Only when in the entertainment hall do male and female patients get the opportunity to mix but even then they sit on opposite sides of the hall with staff watching them like hawks. The hospital is run as two entirely separate entities. The female side is headed up by a Matron and the male side by a Chief Male Nurse. However the real El-Supremo is the Medical Superintendent who rules over all the staff and patients. He lives in a grand house on the main drive with all of the best obsessional patients tending to his garden and doing all the household chores. Most of us students think he's a bit loopy himself. We have watched him from the school window coming up the drive laughing to himself and grimacing. They say it takes one to recognise one.

Day four and tomorrow is my day off. I have been told to take five patients with me to scrub and polish the dormitory floor. So, armed with steaming buckets of hot water, scrubbing brushes, kneeling pads and a selection of patients, I set about the task.

We have pushed to one end of the dormitory the twenty steel framed beds and make a start at the bay window. After about an hour we are halfway down the room. My hands are now wrinkled from the constant use of hot soapy water, they feel terrible and I am lathered with perspiration. This is hard work and my knees are also painful from kneeling on the hard wooden floor. I have noticed during my labours that I have been covering more floor space than the five half-hearted patients working with me. They appear to be tickling the floor rather than scrubbing it. They are more shrewd than I give them credit for. They have scrubbed this floor times without number and think that they are doing just enough to avoid detection and my disapproval. After two hours the job is finished and the wood block floor is scrubbed white. My knees are in a bad way and as I stand up I can hardly straighten my legs. Once I signal that the job is finished the patients are off like a shot, taking their buckets back to the sluice room. I lock the dormitory door behind me and head off for a welcome cup of tea. Thank God I don't have to do this too often. After a cuppa I am told by a staff nurse that I have to go on first lunch; what a relief, I cannot get off the ward quickly enough.

At the top of the main corridor I pass a patient called Darkie who is a long stay patient. He asks me for a fag or some money for a cup of tea. I decline politely giving him my standard response "Don't smoke, stony broke" I know that if I give him even a small amount of money he will pester me every time he sees me. I also know he is quite successful at scrounging especially from visitors. It is rumoured that he has got quite a stash of money hidden somewhere in the ward or the grounds. Some staff are said to watch him very carefully, especially when he is walking outside. I guess that if he has a little pot of gold it will quickly vanish if these nurses find where it is hidden,

As I enter the "Staff Café" for my lunch I notice that Jimmy Seatory, Ron Dullard and another student are already tucking into bangers and mash. I also notice that Bob Russell, a staff nurse, is sitting at a table with several charge nurses. Bob is as usual immaculate in his white coat. He has jet-black hair, sharp chiselled features and very obvious feminine mannerisms. Everyone believes he is homosexual but Bob is a very strong Roman Catholic and keeps his private life very private. He is a brilliant nurse, he does everything by the book and is very kind and attentive to all the patients especially the very old and demented. Suddenly one of the charge nurses picks up a jumbo sausage from his plate and waves it suggestively in front of Bob's face. Bob lets out a high feminine screech and jumps up from the chair with the charge nurse in hot pursuit. He is waving and thrusting the sausage towards Bob's rear end. Bob is half laughing to conceal his embarrassment whilst continuing to scream out effeminately. They both race backwards and forwards around the dining room tables whilst everyone is laughing and a few are clapping and shouting encouragement. The place is in uproar. Not exactly what you might expect in a hospital dining room. Finally the charge nurse tires and the pursuit ends as they both sit down. Peace is restored and staff recommence talking. Although I recognised an element of entertainment in this rather crude spectacle and have joined in the laughter, for me it is an uneasy shallow laugh, to conceal my feelings of embarrassment tinged with sorrow. I feel that Bob has been made to suffer this indignity with forced good grace.

I resume talking to Jim and Ron. Jim has become my best friend in the hospital. He's a few years older than me, balding, of small wiry build with an aquiline nose, a lined forehead and a careworn thin face. He has a great sense of humour and an infectious faked laugh that is more of a social mannerism. One of his attributes is his ability to capture the essence of a situation in a single memorable catch phrase. I remember the creation of one such phrase particularly. It was when we first approached the door to Ward 9, the largest of the geriatric wards. As we neared the door Jim made a grand theatrical gesture by sweeping his hand above his head as if to show a sign above the door and in a loud melodramatic voice announced "OEDEMA

HALL, ABANDON HOPE ALL YE WHO ENTER HERE" According to Jim what this invisible sign says is true in every respect. He says that the ward is virtually the last stop before you pass through the pearly gates. Many old men are admitted to this huge barn-like ward but very few if any ever come out alive. Jim also has another unusual personality trait and that is to occasionally tell blatant lies that are obvious to everyone. One example recently was when we were walking out of the main door to the hospital. He said that his potential father in law who is a businessman had put new wings and sills on his old Ford Prefect and given it a complete re-spray. As we walked down the front steps I spotted his car parked by the side of the road. "Lets see your" I was going to say car but the words froze in my mouth, for the car was as it had been when I last saw it. Rusting sills, battered wings and dull scraped paintwork. When he told me the lie he knew I would see the car within a couple of days. Why does he do it? It's beyond me. He also tells stories that are very colourful and stretch credibility to its limits. Jim isn't alone in this tendency to describe everything in larger than life terms. I do it myself and it is a common tendency in other students. Over egging the cake by using very exaggerated and colourful language can be partly attributed to our natural exuberance and partly to a way of dealing with long hours and long days of boredom. It also helps to lighten our day with its endless domestic work and other forms of drudgery. Boredom is also a reason why staff resort to playing practical jokes on patients, some of which can cause them distress.

Jim's background is also very interesting. He served in the British Army in Korea as a wireless operator and fought in the front line against the Chinese. He and his wife have become close friends of my wife and me and we share many interests. He never appears to take anything seriously although his apparent light hearted attitude belies his keen perception. He has shown me articles in national newspapers about his war exploits and being mentioned in dispatches. According to his wife Olive he still suffers from nightmares from his traumatic experiences in Korea. I have noticed a certain nervousness in his disposition. He is a collection of contradictions, full of bonhomie, yet on some occasions he is a purveyor of pathological untruths for reasons I just cannot comprehend. Ron Dullard sitting opposite me is a very likeable young immature nursing assistant whose lies and exaggerations are even more frequent and more grandiose than Jim's. He owns a Norton Dominator motorbike that he says he has raced in the Isle of Mann TT. He keeps promising me a ride on this super machine that he says will do over a ton. Last week he finally wheeled the bike out for me to ride. When I say I was aghast, that's an understatement. The bike was rusty, the seat was torn, the engine was leaking oil like a sieve. and there were various components held on by wire and tape. Undaunted I mounted the bike and set off down a straight, flat open road. I hadn't gone far before I realised I was taking my life in my hands. From the sound of the engine it was obviously clapped out. After about half a mile I wound back the throttle and watched the speedometer needle slowly creep up to 50 miles per hour. As I reached about 65 mph the speedometer pointer was reluctant to go any further and in fact started to drop back when I reached a slight incline. The engine then started to struggle and sounded as if it was going to seize up so I slowly throttled down, turned round and headed back. As Will came into sight I could see the eager anticipation in his face, possibly he was waiting for the words that would confirm his fantasy that it was indeed a super bike. I got off, leaned the bike towards him and just simply said "great." I thought to myself he is completely cuckoo. He lives in a world of almost total unreality. He appears to see in front of him a brand new Norton Dominator. I see only a clapped out old wreck. Jimmy breaks my train of thought as I hear him recounting to Ron the details of a battle he had fought in Korea. I have heard the account before but still find it interesting. Apparently this well documented battle took place on a large hill known by its geographical coordinates. As he was about to finish the story of his exploits Ron butts in "I flew over that hill on a mission that day in an American

Mustang, I was doing reconnaissance; I must have over flown you." Jim and I give each other knowing looks but don't respond. Ron is at most about 22 and here he is telling us he was flying an American Mustang over a major battlefield in Korea about 8 years ago. This tale certainly tops riding his bike in the Isle of Mann TT. After Ron leaves the table Jim and I express our disbelief at his outrageous statement and have a good laugh. As I walk back down the corridor towards the ward I muse to myself "who is mad in here, the patients or those in the white coats."

Back in the ward I'm informed that the dormitory floor had now dried out and I am instructed to get another group of patients together to polish it. The staff nurse goes to get the polish and I go to the locked cupboard to get the bumpers out. The bumpers have a wooden base; underneath there is an inch thick piece of lead then under that a heavy brush. This makes the bumpers very heavy and unwieldy. Each of my eight selected patients takes a bumper from me and drags it along the floor towards the dormitory. Polishing the entire dormitory floor is another daunting task as it is about 18 feet wide and 50 feet long. However it isn't as bad as scrubbing the damn thing on your hands and knees. The staff nurse as usual has the easy job. He has a large tin containing a mixture of Mansion Polish and a solvent and a piece of stick. He walks up and down the dormitory flicking large dollops of polish on the floor with the stick. At first I find the bumping heavy going until we get all the polish thinly distributed over the floor. As we progress the floor starts to shine and the bumping becomes easier. The knack of using a bumper is to gain some impetus by swinging it as far back as you can and then swinging it in front of you. After about a half hour I get into a rhythm and the click, click, click of the bumpers becomes almost hypnotic and I start to daydream about more interesting things. After an hour we have almost finished. For the final polish we put cloths under the bumpers to produce a high shine. If this building ever caught fire it would burn like a tinderbox with all the polish that has been impregnated into the wood over the years. We then put the beds back in place lining them up by the woodblock pattern on the floor and also ensure that the pillows on each bed are lined up. This type of regimentation pervades the whole male side of the hospital but having recently spent three years in the army I am an expert at bulling and regimentation. I should have been given a medal for it. At present I am not sure if I am training to be a domestic, a waiter, a jailer or a human waste disposal agent. As Jim would rather crudely say "At best we are just lowly shit shovel'ers."

It seems no time since I was at dinner and now tea is up. Tea time passes without incident until we start counting the cutlery back in. Unfortunately we are short of one knife. We do another count and there is still a knife missing. The staff nurse decides to go to Bob's office to report it missing. Bob quickly emerges from his office with a face like thunder. He doesn't like being disturbed and I anticipate another explosion of anger. He stops just outside the office door and gives one sharp command "Strip them all." He then turns, goes back into his office and slams the door. The staff nurse repeats the order and the patients immediately start to strip off; they don't stop until they are all stark naked, not a stitch, even their socks and shoes are discarded. I get the impression by the speed that they undress that this is not the first time this has happened. It's a humiliating sight like I have never seen before, 20 plus men standing at the meal tables stark naked. I doubt if anyone else has seen a sight like this outside a nudist colony or possibly a prisoner of war camp. This is certainly upholding patient's privacy and dignity. We then systematically search every discarded item of clothing. I do it cautiously as putting your hands in some of the patients pockets is rather like putting your hand down a rat hole, you never know what your hand is going to come into contact with. However we find nothing, so with the patients still standing naked we start to search the entire room. All of the tables and chairs are upended. Suddenly one of the nurses exclaims "Got it" as he finds the blade of the knife slotted into a joint on the underside of the table. Mercifully the perpetrator cannot be identified as in the mêlée patients have moved around the room and neither I nor any of the other nurses can remember precisely who was sitting where. There are therefore no repercussions on any individual patient. What a relief. The rest of the shift passes quietly as we watch television until the night staff come on duty at 7.30pm.

Another day another dollar. A diminutive patient has been admitted during my days off. The staff have nicknamed him Titch. I have read his notes to see what is wrong with him and why he has been detained. He certainly doesn't look capable of violence. The story I read in his notes is almost unbelievable. Apparently this tiny thin man who is about 5 feet 2 inches tall stuck an imitation bushy black beard on his chin, got on a high old-fashioned "sit up and beg" bicycle, rode into a village, and held up a Post Office with a toy pistol. Amazingly he made his escape with £2,000.Unfortunately his luck ended there, he was followed and seen to bury his haul in a nearby wood. I am not sure why he hasn't gone to prison but possibly he was found unfit to plead or sent here for an assessment. I found him twice this morning skulking in the far end of the toilet for no apparent reason so I have decided to keep a watchful eye on him.
Another patient is due to be admitted today from the acute admission unit over the road. This is slightly

unusual as people with only a short history of acute mental illness stay over the road in the Collingwood Clinic until they are discharged. This arrangement ensures that any member of the general public who has a breakdown does not get to know that there are two widely diverse standards of care provided, one with very poor standards for those people with chronic mental illnesses, disturbed behaviour or dementia and one with good standards for those people with short term acute illnesses. Another unusual aspect of this new admission is that I have been told he is a black African. He will be the first black patient I have met. When he arrives he is escorted by a nurse from the clinic. As they walk past me I note that he is a very striking looking man, slim, well dressed in smart casual clothes with a very aristocratic, sensitive and pleasant face. He reminds me a bit of Sidney Poitier. To me he also looks slightly schizoid as he doesn't appear to be fully aware of his circumstances or surroundings. I have been told that he is very talented and has had his poetry read on the radio. The patient and his escort both disappear into Bob's office and after a moment or two the nurse emerges and leaves the ward. As I walk through the dining room towards the kitchen the peaceful atmosphere is suddenly shattered by banging and shouting coming from the office, causing me to stop dead in my tracks. It sounds as if chairs are being knocked over and there is a skirmish taking place. Before I decide what to do the office door suddenly opens and the patient comes flying out, staggering forward onto his knees. Bob is right behind him and shouts "That's what you get for fucking nothing, just step out of line once and see what you get." The patient picks himself up and as if in a dream wanders off down the ward. So much for the caring and compassionate admission procedures we are taught in school.

It's afternoon and as instructed I have opened the backs again. The patients scurry past me in single file, hoping to make the toilet before its too late and avoid peeing their pants. When they finish they scurry back to the dayroom much relieved and I check the toilet cubicles one by one to ensure that no one is hiding there. I had noticed that Titch went into the far end toilet and that he was last to leave. Curious I go and look into the toilet cubicle that he has just vacated. There is nothing in the bowl, yet I cannot recall hearing the toilet flush. Still puzzled about what he is up to I pull the handle to make it flush but it doesn't work. I then see what looks like a piece of string sticking out from the u-bend. Intrigued I reach down and put my hand into the bowl and retrieve a small bundle of string like fibres. Looking more closely at the fibres I realise that he has teased them out from the frayed mat near the entrance door. Still mystified I squeeze the water out of the fibres and secrete them in my hand under my white coat. I tell nobody of my find and dispose of the strands in the kitchen waste bin.

On coming out of the kitchen back into the day room I notice that another patient nicknamed Psyche is becoming increasingly disturbed. He is a strange character, with a rather porky appearance. If it were not for his misshapen suit and dishevelled string-like tie outside his shirt collar, he could be mistaken for a well spoken retired bank manager. He has a very odd style of walking which I can best describe as a modified Nazi goose step. The staff have said he definitely has got "the wires on" today. I don't know the origin of this odd description but I guess it comes from the fact that disturbed patients often say they have been wired up and people are reading their thoughts. He has started repeatedly punching himself in the face particularly around his eyes. His cheekbones have become bruised and swollen and look very painful. Despite this he continues to deliver heavy blows to his face, it makes me wince every time he does it. He has been given additional medication but this has had little effect and none of the staff appear concerned. As I leave duty at 7.30 pm he is still at it, one blow after another. His face is now a puffy bruised mess.

Back on duty in the morning after a good night's sleep I have noticed that for some time Michael McComish has been getting more and more restless.

He is his usual pathetic sight wearing the standard patient's uniform, shapeless suit, shoulder pads half way down his shoulders and shrunken trousers half way up his legs. You can tell a patient a mile away by the state of their clothes. Like many other patients Michael's fingers are not just stained with nicotine but black with burns. His lips and the tip of his nose and tongue are similarly burnt from smoking dog ends. Some of the dog ends are so small that he sticks a pin in the butt ends to enable him to hold them to his mouth. I lived with Michael, my father's sister's son, for a short time in a ground floor flat in Suttons Dwelling Tenements Block on Barrack Road near Newcastle United football ground. My grandfather and grandmother on my father's side, who were as poor as church mice, rescued Michael from the orphanage where he had been placed since his mother's death from a brain infection. After she died his father remarried and abandoned Michael and his brothers and sisters in an orphanage. As a young boy Michael was no stranger to violence as his father regularly and unmercifully beat his mother. Michael hated him with a vengeance and vowed to shoot him when he grew up.

In those few months when Michael and I lived together there were nine of us in a flat with three small bedrooms, my father and I, my grandmother, two aunts, one cousin, and two others. Some of the men in the flat worked night shifts and when they got out of bed my dad and I got in. The bed, which was quite dishevelled, was rarely unoccupied. Michael was a few years older than me but I remember him as a quiet boy who loved to spend time playing football with the other kids in the dwellings, some of whom wore raggy clothes and one who that was shoeless. At 17 he and his friend decided to join the regular army together, but unfortunately his friend failed the medical because of flat feet. Michael then found himself alone in the Northumberland Fusiliers. After three months basic training he was sent to fight the communist inspired guerrillas in the jungles of Malaya. Once there he was transferred to the Green Howards. In his letters home he said he was terrified. On occasions he was sent out alone into the jungle to scout or act as a forward sentry. When he told the officer in charge he was frightened and asked for someone to accompany him, permission was refused. I heard later that he had been wounded and invalided out of the service. Curious to know more about what happened to him I went into the office when Bob was out to read his medical records. In his notes it said that he had been ambushed in the jungle by terrorists while he was on night patrol. In the panic and confusion that ensued Michael was shot in the left thorax and left for dead as his unit retreated in disarray. There was confusion surrounding the whole event and it was not certain if he was shot by the terrorists or his own side or if he had fallen and shot himself. Later examination of the powder burns found on his uniform could only establish that the shot was fired at close range. Michael was left in the jungle for three days and nights, seriously wounded, petrified and in severe pain. He was finally found by a group of friendly Malayans and carried back to base camp. He was then transferred to the British Military Hospital at Kinrara in Malaya and put on the dangerously ill list. Later my grandmother received a letter from a colonel at Army Records confirming his injuries. On the 11th October 1950 another letter was received stating he was being transferred from the Dangerously Ill List to the Seriously Ill List. As well as sustaining serious physical injuries Michael had also suffered a total mental breakdown. He was then transferred back to the UK to Netley Military Hospital. On the 19th June 1951 he was finally transferred to this hospital in Newcastle. Here again is another tragic story not dissimilar to that of Tommy Myers. Thankfully my military career had been spent mostly in Nottingham far away from any front line action but I have some understanding of what it must have been like to be uprooted from home in England at the age of 17½ then posted to an inhospitable jungle in an unknown land to fight against an unidentifiable army of ruthless communist guerrillas. Michael has been a victim since his childhood, first from the brutality of his father, then after the death of his mother, from being abandoned by his father and put in an orphanage. The final trauma was being shot and left for dead in the jungle, capped by the final indignity of losing his mind and being placed in this bin exposed to the brutality of some sadistic staff. After his medical discharge from the Army he didn't receive a penny in pension from this so called civilised society. Why? Because Malaya was not classed as a war zone and service there was classified as help to control civil unrest in another country. So far I have not seen anyone ill-treat Michael and I doubt if anyone will while I am working on this ward but I know there can be no guarantees when I finally move from here.

From knowledge of Tommy and Michaels experiences and my own military service I strongly believe that it should be against the law to send anyone under the age of 21 into front line combat. I realise that this may be an unrealistic viewpoint as it is not by accident or omission that very young men are targeted or drafted into fighting in wars against other young men that they have no personal enmity towards. From time immemorial young men have been manipulated in this way and sent out as cannon fodder. When I finally walked out of the army camp to freedom I vowed I would never join any organisation again as they all try to make you conform to the way they say you should think and behave. For me a free and unfettered mind is the greatest asset that anyone can have. I now shy away from most organisations, be they charitable, religious or political.

I notice a newcomer walking towards me through the dining room. The staff nurse tells me that he is the new barber. Apparently he has only been in the job a few weeks. He looks about 5ft 3inches tall and about the same in any other chosen direction. His tummy looks so big that I wait to see how far his outstretched hands will extend beyond his tubby little body. Quite a problem if you are a barber. Nurses have always had the job of cutting patient's hair. Our results vary wildly from being very professional to horrendous basin cuts to almost scalping. My attempts are at present amongst the worst, full of steps and bald spots. However today hopefully all this is about to change. After introducing himself as Bill the barber sets up shop in the day room with a dining room chair and his first client, Buster the Irishman, takes his seat. I notice that the barber is as bald as a coot, very much in contrast to Buster who has a beautiful head of thick grey white hair. Psyche has started to punch himself in the eyes and face again and he is doing himself a lot of damage. His eyes are now reduced to slits in his bruised and battered face. The staff nurse has decided that enough is enough and takes him into the dormitory to pad and bandage his hands to the size of boxing gloves. If this fails they may consider tying his hands to his sides or behind his back.

Michael is also worked up and is pacing the dayroom floor from one end to the other. The barber is distracted by this and looks anxious about this behaviour particularly as Michael is passing within a foot of the chair he is using. Michael makes a quick turn at the end of the ward and strides back towards us. As he passes the barber's chair he lets go a vicious left hook to the jaw of the Irishman. The blow knocks Buster clean off the chair onto the floor. It happens so quickly that the barber is left cutting thin air. Buster staggers to his feet and goes after Michael with a vengeance. Michael spins round to face him but makes no attempt to defend himself as the Irishman punches him to the ground. The staff react quite quickly and pull Buster off before any further damage can be done. I have been told that this is a pattern with Michael; he often attacks the biggest or strongest patients in the ward and then makes no attempt to defend himself. I wonder if this behaviour is linked to his having been shot in Malaya, possibly an attempt to prove himself or maybe it represent a retaliatory attack on his father whom he hated. Titch is still up to his usual trick of threading the carpet and stuffing it down the toilet u-bend and I am still removing it and disposing of it. It's a real cat and mouse game but I still cannot fathom out what reason he has for doing this. I leave duty at the end of my shifts still perplexed about why he is doing it.

My days off are far from relaxing. I have spent the last four days at my part time job making Victorian chandeliers and wall lights for Bamborough's Old Time Music Hall in Newcastle Greenmarket. Back on duty far from relaxed, I hear that during my absence a new patient has been admitted. I first noticed him early in the morning. He appears to be in a dream like state, moving about slowly in an aimless fashion. The general impression he gives me is that he may be rather histrionic and I make a mental note to read his records as soon as possible. Amazingly someone has allocated him to be put on the garden squad. God knows what use he will be out there because he looks too far gone to be of any use.

The rest of the morning passes uneventfully. It's now dinner time and my job after dinner is to ensure that the patients have taken their medication. As I take up my position at the side of the medicine table the staff nurse starts to administer the medication, known colloquially as "Pills to cure all ills" or as others describe them a "chemical cosh or straight jacket." As soon as each patient places his pills on the back of his tongue I give him a glass of water and watch him take a deep gulp. I then ask him to open his mouth wide and stick out his tongue to check thoroughly that he has swallowed them. For several days now I have been suspicious that despite these checks one patient is still secreting tablets in his mouth and I decide to try to catch him out. As he approaches the table I deliberately take a nonchalant none attentive stance. The patient takes his medication and places it very deliberately on the back of his tongue as I hand him a glass of water. He takes a big gulp swallows hard and hands the glass back to me. I then ask him to stick his tongue out which he dutifully does while I give cursory look into his mouth. Indicating that I am satisfied I quickly and deliberately turn my back on him, counting slowly up to five. At the count of five I turn back suddenly just in time to see him putting something in a flower pot on the windowsill. I knew it! He hasn't swallowed his pills at all, the crafty bugger. As I walk towards the window sill he moves furtively away, I think he knows he's rumbled. I pick up the pot and pull out the plant. Clustered all around its roots is a mass of multi coloured tablets. He must have been secreting them there for weeks. In triumph I take the plant with its stash of pills to the staff nurse. He looks surprised and a little awkward as it's his overall responsibility as the trained nurse to ensure that patients take their medication. He then scribbles a reminder to make a request to the doctor for the patient to be put on liquid medication.

It's staff after lunch rest time and Bob the charge nurse has occupied his usual chair in the day room. I am sitting a few yards away from him with a staff nurse. The new patient is lounging on a large leather settee almost directly opposite me. Slowly he starts to slither off the settee onto the floor. The staff nurse next to me mutters something under his breath, puts his paper down, gets up and crosses the floor towards the patient. None too gently he pulls the patient up by his lapels and roughly pushes him back on the couch. As he walks back to his seat and sits down, the patient again slithers off the couch onto the floor. The staff nurse gets up quickly and strides across the floor again. This time he uses more force exclaiming, "fuck you" as he puts him back on the settee. At this point I have spotted Bob glancing from behind his newspaper. I sense his increasing irritability and steel myself for an explosion. Again the patient slithers onto the floor and the staff nurse picks the him up and this time throws him with such force into the back of the heavy settee that it almost topples over backwards. At this point Bob jumps up, strides across the day room, unlocks the door to the backs and disappears from view. Moments later he emerges carrying a white enamel bucket full of water. He marches across the floor towards the patient and launches the bucket of water full into his face and chest. Not satisfied with this he rams the empty bucket over the patient's head. The patient still doesn't react or make a sound but within moments again slithers off the chair onto the floor, the bucket falling off his head with a clang. Bob's face now looks grim, a look which I am now quite familiar with. With a wave of his arm he summons the staff nurse for assistance and they both then drag the soaking patient, by his jacket collar, on his back across the floor and into the toilet area. From my seat in the day room I can hear the sounds of water running full bore. After several minutes I hear Bob calling out McCarthy and I respond immediately. As I enter the backs near the washbasins I can see Bob and the staff nurse through the bathroom door. I see that they are holding the fully clothed patient under the water in the bath. He is struggling wildly trying to get a grip on the bath sides but they keep knocking his hands off and continue to hold him under. After a while they bring him to the surface, let him splutter and gasp for a moment and then push him forcibly under the water again. After repeating this process several more times they appear to be satisfied with the punishment they have inflicted and haul him up. As they walk past me out of the bathroom Bob curtly says to me "get him some fucking clothes." I quickly go to the ward store and get him a complete set of clothing and return to the bathroom. The patient is just standing mute by the bath with water running from his clothes. He is shaking from head to foot possibly from a mixture of cold, shock and fear; I cannot tell which but most possibly it's the freezing cold water. Quickly I remove all his sodden clothes and very inadequately try to reassure him in a sympathetic tone saying that I'm sorry for what has happened. As I towel him down he doesn't show any response but just stares vacantly ahead. Now that he is in dry clothes I realise that I haven't got a change of socks or shoes for him. I know that these are locked in a special cupboard and that only the charge nurse has the key. As I look for Bob I see that he hasn't returned to his seat in the day room. The office is the obvious place to look so I make a bee-line for there. The door to his office is open but I still dutifully knock. He responds with an agitated "YES" As I enter he is sitting with his feet on the desk reading a newspaper. Deferentially I tell him I have dried the patient and changed his clothes but I need the keys to get the patient some dry socks and shoes. He looks at me with disdain and replies "What do you think this is fucking Butlins Holiday Camp, send him out as he is". As I leave the office I look across the ward and out of the window; it is a cold miserable day and I feel sorry and powerless to do anything to help the patient further. 15 minutes later he is out working in sodden socks and shoes in the bitterly cold gardens until about 4.00 pm.

Several thoughts pass through my mind when I witness extreme cruelty of this type. The first is the irony of consultant medical staff continually banging on in the national media about the savage treatment meted out to Russian dissidents who are wrongfully detained in Russia's psychiatric hospitals and the drugs and electro-convulsive therapy forced on them.

Here in Britain they are totally silent about what is occurring right under their noses, either because they are ignorant or because, like us they dare not or do not want to speak out. It has also occurred to me that at least the Russian hierarchy have come up with the lame excuse that their dissidents are socially deviant or are trying to subvert the state. No such excuse exists here, our people here are just unfortunately mentally ill. The second and more personally disturbing question I ask myself is what is my position here. For instance what if there were no controls at all here, how far would these cruel nurses go and more importantly how far would I let them go before I found the courage to speak up to try to put a stop to their brutality. The honest answer that comes into my head is not one I can be proud of. I actually don't know how bad it would have to get before I say this far but no further. During the war captured German death camp guards said by way of excuse that they were just following orders. The price for them to disobey would have been very severe, at worst they would have been shot by firing squad, or at least interned themselves or sent to an almost certain death in the front line. What then is my excuse for not speaking up? The worst thing that could happen to me would be to be sacked. At the least it might lead to me being blacklisted, given bad reports and sent to Coventry. I fully realise that rationalisation is the order of the day here and I and all the other good nurses use it as a way to avoid doing anything. It's a wonderful mechanism for stifling action and salving your conscience. It goes like this. I say to myself if I ever get into a position of responsibility the only people I will show no mercy to are those guilty of ill-treating or neglecting patients. However I recognise this for what it is, a fantasy. I am not even sure I am going to pass my final exams, never mind being in a position of power or authority. Another rationalisation is that I will never hide or deny the things I have witnessed here and one day I will write about what life is really like here. My poor ability at spelling and English will most likely put paid to that grand idea. The ultimate rationalisation is to believe that things are steadily getting better and if we just hang on, in the fullness of time the cruelty will come to an end and patients will get the care and treatment they deserve. So sit tight keep your head down and it will all go nicely away. What goes on here is an open secret, everybody is in on it. I know that the nurse managers are unlikely to witness individual acts of cruelty but they have all come up through the ranks and some of the older nurses have told me that "Things were a lot worse here in the old days" The doctors are detached and appear only to be interested in academia or in the acute patients across the road in the Collingwood Clinic. For them seeing chronically ill patients appears to be a chore and one of the few downsides of being a psychiatrist. Thinking about it I have been here for nearly two years now and I have never spoken a single word to a doctor. To cap it all the Medical Superintendent is a complete cuckoo. The consequence of all this is that my student friends and I are firmly convinced that we cannot buck the system. We stand no chance against the combined power of the doctors, managers, charge nurses, and the Union. Who would believe us? What evidence could we produce? Even in those instances where patients are injured by staff we all know how easy it is to record these occurances as self-harm, an accident, the result of having to be restrained or as a consequence of a fight with another patient. We are aware that we could not even rely on other staff witnesses to back us up. So it does not stretch the imagination to understand why we all stand by and watch and hold our tongues. The system here is watertight.

Freddy McGurn has started banging on the windows in the dining room. One of the staff nurses quickly strides up to him, spins him around by the shoulder and sinks two heavy punches into the pit of his stomach. Freddy gasps and doubles up onto the floor. The nurse strides away and returns with a 10 ml glass of paraldehyde, which Freddy gratefully gulps down. It's all in a day's work, part of the excellent treatment of the mentally ill. The rest of the shift passes without further incident. At 7.30 pm I wearily hang up my white coat in the locker room and walk down the corridor past the locked security rooms where the most difficult patients are bedded down for the night. I hope that their dreams are better than the reality of their waking hours. Out in the cold fresh air I take a deep breath and head for home.

Today they have moved me downstairs to an open ward where the patients are more independent. Apparently they are short of staff due to sickness. The ward is run by Charge Nurse McGregor He's another built like a tank. He also has a fearsome reputation but from my observations this morning he treats the patients very well and speaks to them in a kindly manner. John Savage, an experienced staff nurse colloquially known as the Stick Man, has just come in from the side door, He's come to round up his squad of patients for garden duties. One of their tasks involves collecting broken tree branches in a wheel barrow, hence John's nickname Stick Man. His group also tidies up flower borders and does a bit of planting. When they leave the ward it is very quiet with only a few patients remaining. I feel that it's going to be a long monotonous morning. One patient who has remained on the ward has started creating a bit but nothing excessive. I have never seen him before. He's about 30 which is young for this type of ward. I would describe him as thin and weedy and he looks rather like a bookworm. He's been whining persistently in a pathetic high pitched voice for about ten minutes now. He wants to go home for the weekend. Apparently it's about two weeks since he last had leave even though he lives quite near to the hospital. Bill the staff nurse working with me has repeatedly told him that when the doctor visits the ward he will ask if he is prepared to grant the leave. As I'm chatting to Bill a nurse whom I don't recognise comes down the ward corridor towards us. He asks Bill if he can borrow some medication as they have run out on his ward. As I step to one side they start to have chat and a laugh together. The whining patient approaches them and again asks if he can go home. Bill tells him to wait but the patient persists. "Please I want to go home" In response Bill rounds on the patient and in a loud voice says "Bugger off" but undaunted the patient repeats his request. Bill responds with a question "You live at 22 Brights Road don't you; the patient looking slightly puzzled replies yes. "The one with the green door;" the patient again replies yes. "Your wife's that little dark haired thing." again the patient replies yes. "With the big titties." This time the patient does not respond. Bill's in full swing now, "I shagged her last night while you were locked up in here". This time the patient responds quickly, "No you didn't you're a liar". Bill responds in an even nastier fashion "She couldn't get enough of me, we were at it all night". Bill is now getting very vindictive. The patient starts to become emotional too shouting "you're a liar, it's not true." Bill responds again "Oh yes it is and I'm going to see her again this weekend and give her one". The patient is now almost beside himself and in distress and anger shouts, "you're a liar, a liar, liar". Suddenly without warning Bill launches a punch straight into the side of the patients face. The patient staggers back with the impact and falls to the floor holding his face crying and whimpering. Without a flicker of emotion Bill turns and continues his conversation with the visiting nurse, who also looks totally impassive and unperturbed. The patient slowly picks himself up, holding his face and quietly moves away to the far end of the ward. Quite wisely he has decided to put as much distance as possible between him and Bill. Later in the day as I reflect yet again on this act of savagery including the total lack of reaction from the visiting nurse; I find it very difficult to believe that Bill who I previously thought was quite a gentle fun person could incite the patient in such a hurtful way and then viciously attack him when he responded with justifiable anger and distress. I also reflect on my own apparent lack of reaction and realise that although I was inwardly shocked and appalled I too remained impassive. Bill must assume that the other nurse and I were fully accepting or unperturbed by his behaviour. This calculated lack of reaction may be one of the factors that sustain the systematic brutality throughout the male side of the hospital. The next few hours pass slowly and uneventfully. There has been no sign of the doctor, maybe this was just a lie Bill told the patient to shut him up. Whatever the situation is by the end of the shift the doctor hasn't visited and the patient is deprived of the prospect of a weekend at home. I am now starting to wonder how Bill was so familiar with the description of the patient's wife and the home address. It's especially puzzling that he knew the house had a green door. He could have got the address from the file and might have seen the wife when she visited the ward but he could not have known about the green door unless maybe he was trying to seek her out with predatory intentions. It wouldn't be a new phenomenon in this place if he was.

The next few shifts are uneventful and my four days off duty have arrived quickly. The weather is cold for November with a bitter wind blowing from the northeast. The only heating in my house is from an open fire in the living room, the rest of the house is like an igloo. My first two days off have been spent at my part time job across the river Tyne at Gateshead. Yesterday when I went to the works back door I saw a youth trying to kick-start my motorbike in the car park. Unfortunately he saw me running towards him and dropped the bike like a hot brick and legged it. Lucky for him I didn't catch him and lucky for me he didn't manage to steal it.

For the next few days I have been working on the house as I have been doing for nearly two years now.

It doesn't look much different, it's a Forth Bridge Job. Thank God tomorrow I will be back at work.

Its 5.30 am and it's my first day back at work. Its pitch black outside. The windows are completely frosted over as I leave my bed to snatch a quick cup of tea and a slice of toast. I quickly climb into my freezing cold motorbike clothes. They are a strange assortment, a German Army forage cap with earflaps, a pair of World War II British fighter pilot's goggles and a British Army officer's rubberised trench coat. The only authentic bit of kit is my pair of proper leather motorbike gloves that cost me a bomb. Careful not to waken my wife I step out into the blackness of a frost laden winter morning. The breath from my mouth billows out in a cloud of condensation as I scrape the glistening frost off the bike seat. I kick the engine over twice and it splutters into life. Ease of starting is one good thing about these James 197cc two strokes. By the time I have travelled about 2 miles I am frozen to the bone, even my hands within my gauntlets are numb and I have to pull all my fingers into the centre of the gloves to keep them warm. Two miles further on as I approach a set of traffic lights about half a mile from the hospital I am aware of a queue of dark Lowry like figures huddled at a bus stop on the opposite side of the road. I touch the brakes and throttle down and without warning the bike shoots from under me.. Black ice Bugger! Within a split second I am down

76

on the road, the bike's in front of me shooting along on it's side showering me with sparks from it's contact with the road. I follow close behind on my backside with my feet in the air in front of me. In this a ridiculous and undignified fashion I travel the full length of the bus queue before the bike and I come to a halt. None of the people in the bus queue moves, nobody comes to my assistance. I get to my feet and try to raise the bike but suddenly my feet shoot from under me and I'm down again. The road is like an ice rink. Two further attempts to get on my feet end with the same results. Finally I manage to raise the bike and keep my balance. Pushing it to the side of the road, I check myself up and down, no pain no blood, I don't appear to have suffered any harm. The bike's handlebars are a bit wonky and the footrest is bent upwards. It could have been worse. I gingerly walk the bike across the traffic lights, straighten the handlebars as best I can and get back on the bike. For the rest of the journey I stay at about 10 miles per hour with my left leg sitting awkwardly on top of the bent footrest. Not the best of starts to my first day back on duty. When I finally arrive at the ward changing room and take my trench coat off, I see that there's a large hole in the rear. I realise that had it not been for the heavy-duty rubberised coat the hole would have been in my trousers, or worse still in my backside.

Back on the ward I am told that quite a lot has happened during my four days off. A new black

Nursing Assistant called Vince has started on the ward. He is the first coloured person on the hospital staff. I also hear that Titch has escaped and legged it. He had planned his escape well. Apparently he avoided the vigilance of the nurses and got himself locked in the toilets. To stop the staff getting in after him he had taken strands of carpet that he had secreted down the toilet during my days off and tied the inside handle of the entrance door to the nearby washbasin taps. He then removed a wooden toilet seat and used it to smash his way through the window, finally climbing down the drainpipe to make his escape. When the staff heard the windows being broken and realised what was happening they couldn't open the door. Now I understand what his intentions had been all along. He had fooled me completely. So I decide that discretion is my best option and never mention my little cat and mouse game with him, particularly as the thought has now occurred to me that he could have had a more serious intention for collecting the strands. He could have intended to hang himself or less likely to garrotte the lone night nurse or another patient. I have been told that there is no evidence that he is mentally ill therefore there is no need to have him back here. If he is caught it is likely that he will go straight to prison.

Vince the newcomer and I hit it off immediately although we couldn't be more different. Of course he is black or as I would prefer to describe him dark brown. He is about 6ft 2 inches tall and he looks like a bronzæd Greek God, whereas I am pasty white, 5ft 10 and of a thin sinuous build. But we share a great number of things in common, primarily a strong sense of humour, a laid back attitude, a liking for girls, partying, swimming and weight lifting. After a few days of getting to know each other he has asked me if I would like to go with him to an illegal drinking den in the West End of Newcastle and I have said yes I would jump at the chance. I have reciprocated by offering to take him to some parties being held by my friends.

There has been an influx of new nursing assistants over the last year. They are a mixed and colourful bag. Hungarians escaping from their country after their thwarted revolution against the Russians. A group from down south rumoured to be criminals who are here to hide away from the grasp of the police. A small group of male homosexuals has also joined the staff. The most flamboyant of them is Vivian. He's a big bloke with dyed yellow blond hair and quite a muscular frame. He appears to have two permanently limp wrists both of which are festooned with heavy gold bracelets. He wears black eye liner and blue eye shadow with a slight trace of lipstick. I don't know how he gets away with it on duty but he does. I've worked a few shifts with him and I like him. He's very loud and extroverted and there's never a dull moment with him. He is great with the patients, both kind and considerate. There are so many inconsistencies in the way people view homosexuals in this society. Firstly homosexual practices are illegal. Over the road at the Collingwood Clinic psychiatrists and psychologists are showing homosexuals pictures of naked men and shocking them with electricity in the vain hope that they will induce in them a lasting aversion to male to male sex. What a hope! Why don't they just give them psychotherapy to help to get rid of their unnecessary guilt and help them to adjust and feel happy about their sexuality. After all we have very well adjusted male and female homosexual nurses working here in the hospital doing a great job. The inconsistencies are glaring and perplexing. Alan my homosexual friend shed even more light on these inconstancies and double standards. He informed me of a number of nurses that he had sexual dalliances with. The list was quite long and contained several surprises. The list contained well known homosexual staff but also a number of older married nurses and others that were well known as womanisers. At first I thought he might just be boasting or telling me the names of heterosexuals to clear the ground before making an approach towards me. As for clearing the way to come on to me I thought this was unlikely and he never did make an approach. Unfortunately for him making such an approach would have strained what was a good friendly relationship between us.

Its 7 am and I am back on duty totally knackered, Vince took me to an illegal basement drinking den in a large house in the West End last night. It was only a short distance from the "Blue Lamp" police station. The place was packed and the music ear bursting. All the people there were black African and I was the only white man present although there were a few white girls. The basement was bare of furniture and felt dank and smelt musty. In one corner was a makeshift bar made from upturned crates with planks of wood on top. The music was fantastic, very African with a heavy drum beat. It maybe a cliché to say that all black people have inbuilt rhythm but here it certainly was true, they were all wonderful dancers. Vince introduced me to all of his friends who were in great spirits and enjoying themselves. I had a great time and was sorry to leave when the party was still in full swing. We finally staggered out at 2 am to walk the 5 miles back home.

At a second similar party I was again the only white man present. On this occasion I decided to go in casual clothes, only to find out that it was a smart suit and tie event. Strangely it was not my whiteness that bothered me but being in the wrong style of dress. But my composure was restored during the playing of the hit song "The Locomotion" when a friend of Vince's complimented me on my dancing.

To be complimented on my dancing in this company was a high honour indeed. Again we had a great time and Vince and I left after midnight to stagger the five miles home

Another party Vince and I attended in an upstairs flat was mainly for hospital staff. It ended in fisticuffs and a few injuries. It was about an hour into the party and a lot of alcohol had been consumed. Sitting next to me at a table was a nurse I knew. Fred was the one that had claimed that a patient's father had held him while the patient knocked out his two front teeth. All of a sudden he stood up and punched the male nurse opposite him full in the face. Within seconds all hell had broken loose. Several nurses jumped on Fred's back in an attempt to drag him to the floor. They were hanging round his neck while he swung them backwards and forwards as if they were ribbons on a maypole. As they were getting nowhere I stepped in and kicked Paddy behind the knees bringing them all down with a resounding crash to the floor. As they were subduing him I heard someone banging on the front door. When I opened the door the woman from the ground floor flat started shouting in my face "Stop the noise my children are historical." I thought to myself yes she got something there, all children are historical. I reassured her that we would not cause any further commotion, and went back upstairs to quieten things down. However before I was able to achieve this there was another knock on the door and this time it was the police. When I opened the door the officer pushed past me and went quickly upstairs. He informed everyone that if we did not cut the noise out and behave we would all be arrested. As soon as the policeman had gone Vince and I decided we had seen and heard enough and made a quick exit. Once outside Vince said "What was all that about, why did he punch that bloke?" I replied "I haven't got a clue." Glad to be free of the turmoil and the possibility of being arrested we quickly made tracks for home. Later a nurse told me that this behaviour wasn't uncommon when Paddy had a few drinks. They speculated it was a form of mania-au-partue, a condition where even quiet people can become violent and aggressive when they are under the influence of alcohol.

Back working on the ward this morning I feel shattered by last night's revelry and over indulgence. Unfortunately it is the dreaded bath day again but I am lucky this time in having escaped the worst part of the job, which is supervising the bathing and washing the patient's hair. My allocated task is to act as the runner, collecting the dirty clothes and towels and ensuring that there is a steady supply of clean ones. About fifteen patients have now been bathed and we are more than half way through the task. Two staff and two patients are currently in the bathroom. I think it's about time to check how things are going. As I enter the bathroom I see two staff nurses with a large bath towel wrapped around the neck of Jimmy the masochist. Each has hold of one end of the towel pulling it tight. To get more leverage each has a foot pressed against one of the two baths. Jimmy is cackling and grimacing maniacally and trying to get his hands between the towel and his neck to relieve the pressure. The nurses laugh as Jimmy struggles to get free. Finally his legs begin to buckle and he starts to slump towards the floor. The nurses then release the towel and appear to have enjoyed the game. Jimmy regains his senses and his balance and grabs his clothes and scuttles away to get dressed, apparently unconcerned and unharmed. The two nurses then continue with the bathing, again as if nothing wrong has happened.

For a week now we have had a tall young man in the ward called Willy. He's not very bright and has gained the reputation of being a bit of a whiner by constantly asking for his mother and crying to go home. During bathing time he has been making a lot of noise and has been repeatedly pestering staff. I sense that the patience of some of them is wearing thin. Bob comes out of the office with his usual grim face and the boy turns his attention to him. Big mistake! Bob tells him to piss off but he persists in crying to go home. Bob brushes him aside and this time tells him to fuck off but the boy is not put off and continues to pester him. Without a further word

Bob jumps on him from behind and puts him onto the floor in a sitting position. Willy seems to know what is coming and starts to struggle violently. Bob is unsuccessfully trying to apply a firm neck lock, while Willy continues to thrash about on the floor. Bob is part kneeling with his down-turned face quite close to my right side. I clench my fist. From this position I could easily put one right on his jaw and floor him. As soon as the thought enters my head I realise the thought for what it is, a fantasy, a further rationalisation on my part. Sure I could easily do it, but no way am I going to stick one on the end of the charge nurse's chin and end my and career. So I quickly dismiss the idea from my mind. As the scuffle continues Bob also ends up on his backside and two staff nurses go to his aid. One lies across the patient's legs while the other loosens his hands from Bob's arms where the patient has been trying to frustrate Bob's efforts to apply a firm neck lock. Bob finally manages it and starts to tighten his grip. Suddenly there is the sound of a key in the lock of the dormitory door and I see a doctor looking intently at the scene through the glass. He opens the door and walks towards us. As he walks past, Bob looks up from the floor but remains holding the patients neck. The doctor looks down casually and says "Epileptic fit?" Bob replies "yes, self induced." The doctor walks on casually towards the office, apparently unconcerned. The appearance of the doctor has given Bob a new priority so he releases his grip on Willy's neck and goes to attend to the doctor. Willy hasn't come off too badly this time. Let's hope he has sufficient sense not to upset Bob again.

Lunch time arrives and I am supervising the tables. Suddenly a patient falls off his chair taking his plate and its contents with him, splattering all over his clothes and the floor. He then goes into a full grand-mal seizure. Another nurse and I quickly hold his head and limbs to prevent any further damage while someone runs to get a rubber gag to place between his teeth to prevent him from biting his tongue. This is not an unusual occurrence as we have three or four patients here with severe epilepsy. Several full blown fits a week are fairly commonplace. There are some occasions when patients will come out of one fit and go straight into another. This is called status epilepticus and it is a serious condition which can be life threatening. Luckily this patient has only sustained a slight abrasion on his forehead and he is starting to regain consciousness. We help him to his feet and half walk half carry him into the dormitory to rest on his bed until he fully recovers.

After lunch we start the boring job of bumping the dayroom floor, Psyche is still far from well and his cheeks are still very red and swollen. He is pacing the floor in his usual characteristic modified Nazi goosestep. One of the staff gives him a bumper and he still manages to use it despite his padded and bandaged hands. Suddenly he smacks himself in the face with the end of the heavy bumper pole, then again and again. One of the staff shouts "Go on Psyche you're hitting the right man." I manage to intervene quickly and grab a tight hold on the pole while he struggles to hit himself again. A staff nurse joins me and Psyche is then unceremoniously frog marched off into the dormitory by two staff members. A few minutes later he emerges with his hands bandaged to his sides. It's certainly all go here today.

Just before tea time Albert the obsessional has brought up the meal trolley and left it in the kitchen. I give a bit of a sigh as I hear shouting coming from the kitchen. Jesus, here we go again. Suddenly two staff nurses emerge from the kitchen each holding a patient's arm behind his back. They move away from me propelling him from behind down the corridor in a zigzag fashion, first smacking him into one wall and then into the opposite wall. Each time he is about to hit the wall the patient manages to turn his head to one side and avoid the impact on his face. Luckily for him they only do this three or four times, I guess that this is because the amount of effort required is difficult to sustain. As they let him go they are both out of breath. Apparently while they were in the kitchen the patient sneaked in and grabbed some of the food from right under their noses. The patient slinks warily past me through the dining room into the day room and although he appears winded he doesn't seem to have sustained any physical damage. This patient never shows any particular emotion and is reputed by staff to be masochistic and apparently almost immune to pain.

Tea is now over without incident and the medication has been dished out. The daily routine is finished and it's now settling down time for the staff. The TV is on and almost everyone is seated comfortably and looking forward to a few hours viewing until the night staff coming on duty. Unfortunately not Willy, he is kicking up again and I can see that he is starting to get on the nerves of some of the staff. I know now from experience that this will lead to repercussions for him. So I decide to approach him to try to distract him by engaging him in conversation. My attempt however is futile; he knows that I am of no significance and breaks away from me to follow a senior member of staff. At this point I see Bob the charge nurse wandering up the ward from his office. If I was in the prediction business I would make a fortune. Sure enough Willy spots him and makes a beeline for him, whining loudly as he goes. Here we go again, Bob brushes him roughly aside and signals to the two staff nurses. They all close in on Willy, the two staff nurses grab Willy's legs and Bob grabs him under the arms. Willy is quite a big lad but the nurses are strong physically. Without too much effort they lift him horizontally in the air as he struggles and kicks his legs. They jerk him to their chest height then simultaneously drop him horizontally on to his back. He hits the floor with a heavy thud that completely knocks the wind out of him but before he can recover they pick him up and drop him again. One final lift and down he goes for the third time. They now seem satisfied that they have silenced him and taught him a lesson. They walk away leaving Willy making muffled sobs on the floor. All this brutality definitely registers with the other patients but they don't show any sign of being bothered or concerned, possibly because they have seen this type of thuggery many times before or maybe because they fear the staff and don't want to bring any unwanted attention to themselves. When I asked a more approachable member of staff "How come quieter staff never seem to get into conflicts and fights with patients?" he replies that it's because we, the tougher more experienced staff make the rules and enforce them vigorously. He goes on to say that the use of physical punishment engender in the patients a total fear of staff" he then adds, "This protects you and other staff like you. You should consider yourself lucky that the patients here fear anyone in a white coat." As I reflect on his reply I recall that I was present at the time when one discharged aggressive psychopath returned to see the staff. He had initially been very violent and as a consequence had received several beatings from the charge nurse and other members of staff. After these punishment beatings he had become much quieter and had actually become one of the ward trusties before he was discharged. On the day he came back to see us he had sat down at the tea table with the staff. During the conversation that followed he had looked with admiration at the charge nurse and said "Those hammerings you gave me were the best thing that ever happened to me, they really straightened me out" At the time I found his remark quite disconcerting as it appeared to confirm the effectiveness of Bob's brutal approach. It certainly did not fit comfortably with my view that care and compassion are the proper and most effective ways to treat patients. However I recall from my time in the army that many of the full time soldiers with stripes on their arms were basically psychopaths. They thrived on strict, harsh discipline and they had no time for so called softies.

It is now nearing the end of the shift and with a sigh of relief I sit down with one eye on the TV and the other on the patients. You can never totally relax in here and I have felt a low grade headache coming on which I hope will not get worse. The television is rubbish tonight and I cannot settle to watch it. On the empty chair next to me I spot a Union magazine and pick it up. As I flick indifferently through the pages I see a picture of Bob standing at a podium,.

giving a talk at a C.O.H.S.E. National Conference. When I read what he had been saying I could puke, talk about hypocrisy. He is recorded as saying that "these poor unfortunates have nothing to do" and the solution should be to introduce some activity into the wards. Something like industrial therapy. He is further quoted as saying that industrial therapy would bring with it the dignity of work and wages for patients. It beggars belief how he can stand up and say this at a Conference and then knock seven bells out of defenceless patients here in this ward. It's certainly another lesson for me about the hypocrisy and deviousness of human behaviour. However it's obvious to me that there must be something in it for him, possibly another bit of empire building. Back here in the hospital he uses his Union muscle to block every progressive move forward. Currently he is mobilising his shop stewards and sheep-like members to resist the integration of male and female staff. He doesn't even want female cleaners on the male wards. Why I cannot fathom. Maybe he sees it as possibly leading to the end of his Union's dominance, as most of the female nurses either don't belong to a trade union or are members of the Royal College of Nursing. Certainly if there was integration the male staff would be the main beneficiaries as they generally have a greater continuity of service which would facilitate more opportunities for promotion. Part of his agenda is quite simple and transparent, it's to build an alternative power base for himself against management and to defend it at all costs. I put the magazine down and look at him sitting opposite me. In my view he is without doubt the most ambitious, articulate and cruel psychopath I have come across.

Several weeks later, I knew it! This morning large boxes are being brought into the ward. They are marked with the name of a well known, over the counter, painkiller. The dawn of industrial therapy has arrived by courtesy of Bob the philanthropist. No sooner is breakfast finished than the dining room tables are brought into the dayroom and lined up end to end. The chairs are arranged around as Albert and another patient stagger in with two more large boxes. When they are opened I see they contain thousands of neatly packed cardboard cards. Bob is there supervising and starting to empty the cards in piles onto the table. Each individual card is square and partly perforated and we are shown our part of the process which is to tear around the perforation to reveal the outline of a pillbox that can then be fully assembled. Bob gives a deft demonstration and then continues stacking them in front of us like casino chips. Ten minutes later we are at it full blast. It's unremitting until lunchtime with only a short mid morning break for coffee. Dinner comes and goes and we are back at the table again tearing around the perforations. Teatime seems a mile away but it also comes and goes and we are back at it again. Come seven o'clock we are finally finished. It's been 8 hours of mind-stunning bum numbing tedium. My forefinger and thumb are red and quite sore. 7.30pm arrives and I cannot get off duty quickly enough. On the way home I think to myself "So this is the great innovation for restoring the dignity of patients." Somehow I doubt it!

This week has felt as if time has stood still. Almost every hour of every working day we have been tearing up cardboard. I now have blisters on my forefinger and thumb and nobody will convince me that it's therapeutic for the patients to be forced to sit still all day. It's rumoured that for some reason Bob is in competition with another charge nurse to produce the greatest output. I am not sure what is behind it all but it could be a back hander from the firm or something less obvious. What I do know is that Bob will have a well thought out reason for wanting to win this race. As far as the patients are concerned I am not sure what is the more soul destroying, the usual enforced idleness or this enforced form of slave labour. The large completed boxes are stacking up in one of the side rooms and Bob is intent on keeping up the pace of production. The competing charge nurse doesn't stand a chance. He will lose, that's for certain. However this is my last week on the ward and next week I will be in school; what a relief.

One very unusual development took place today. For the first time a woman has started work on the ward. Knowing Bobs virulent resistance to even having women in any part of the male side of the hospital this is truly a puzzling event. She is a slim pretty young women who appears to be rather shy and nervous. She is so slim in fact that her overall almost goes round her twice. She has light hair done up in a bun. Her makeup is a little overdone particularly her eye shadow and eyeliner but her effect on the male staff is dramatic. They have stopped swearing and are behaving impeccably towards the patients. They escort her everywhere she goes on the ward to ensure she is safe. When she cleans the dormitory the staff make sure that all of the patients are out and then lock the door behind her to ensure she is safe and undisturbed. Even Bob Vickerstaff is on his best behaviour. Having now seen how her presence has improved the behaviour of the staff I feel that all of my thoughts about doing away with single sex wards have been justified. The only unfortunate aspect on this ward is that there is only one female and she is only on duty for short periods of time

Tonight I am taking Vince to a party arranged by a friend of mine. He has been to several of my friends parties before but .there is one problem worrying me and that is that at least two of my friends wives have had affairs with him and one is now possibly pregnant by him. If the baby is black then the balloon will go up when the baby arrives. I have seen the magnetic effect Vince has on women and tonight I guess there will be another woman who will throw herself at him. Hey Ho here we go again.

It's my second last day on the ward and I have just been down for the newspapers from the nursing admin office. Small groups of workmen have started digging up the oak blocks from the corridor floor and piling them outside the back of building. I asked one of the men what was going on and he said they were going to replace the wood parquet floor with lino.

When I get back to the ward the staff nurse tells me that a patient nicknamed King Smith is being transferred here from the sick ward. I remember him from when I was working with Jimmy in the Collingwood Clinic. It was there that I first met King Smith and it was nearly our last meeting. He and his wife have a strange psychological relationship They both share a very rare condition called Folie a deux. I have been told that this is a an illness where the dominant partner in a close relationship who suffers from paranoid schizophrenia, passes on his or her delusional ideas to the submissive partner. Apparently if they are separated for a reasonable length of time the submissive partner recovers whereas the dominant partner continues to experience the delusions. In

King Smith's case he believes that he is the heir to the throne of England but not as a male member of the royal family but, stranger still, as a female member. He has handwritten a voluminous rambling book staking his claim to the throne. Its title is King Smith and the Stone of Scone. His wife has absorbed his delusions and is totally convinced of his claim. My first encounter with King Smith was the most traumatic event I have experienced since I started training. It was when Jim and I were on early shift in the ward kitchen preparing for breakfast on the acute admission ward at the Collingwood Clinic. We had been told at early morning handover that King Smith had been very disturbed during the night and as a consequence had been placed in the padded cell at the end of the corridor. Jim and I decided to go and see if he was alright and set off down the corridor. When we reached the padded cell door I pulled back the two spring loaded bolts and swung it open. The sight that greeted us was horrendous. There was blood splattered everywhere, over the floor and up the padded walls. King Smith was on his back on the floor facing us, he had broken a saucer in half and was sawing through his neck with the jagged edge. There was a large gaping wound in his neck and he was gurgling but still fully conscious. Jim grabbed the slippery saucer and wrenched it from his grasp and threw both halves out through the door, into the corridor. We were both shouting in panic for help but the confines of the room and the padded walls were absorbing most of the sound. Jim swivelled round on the blood soaked floor and got his head outside the door and shouted down the corridor for help. I held King Smith's blood soaked hands as best I could as he was trying to get his fingers into the wound to pull it further apart. I took off my white coat and used it to try to stem the blood. Two trained staff arrived, breathing hard, and took over. I don't know how King Smith got a saucer, maybe the night staff gave him an early morning cup of tea with a saucer. He should have been watched while he drank it and both cup and saucer should have been retrieved. We heard later that King Smith had miraculously survived and that later he had been returned to us from surgery at the General Hospital. He was then placed in our sick ward within the main building. It was there that I met him for the second time. He was confined to bed and heavily sedated. We had to take it in turns to be by his bed on two-hour shifts throughout the day and night. His neck was heavily bandaged not just because of the large wound but because at every opportunity he tried to undo the bandages. He also continually tried to get his fingers under the bandages to unpick the stitches in his neck. At times when he was most persistent we had to tie his wrists to the bed as the only alternative would have been to wrestle with him continually day and night. He was the most intensely suicidal patient I have ever encountered. Many weeks later when I left the sick ward he had still not improved and now here I am awaiting for my third encounter with him. He has obviously recovered physically but to be transferred to this ward means that he must still be very psychologically disturbed. As I leave for lunch he still hasn't arrived.

Walking up the main corridor towards the dining room I see that the workmen have made good progress removing the wood floor blocks and as I pass one of the corridor window I see that they are burning them just outside the building. What a waste; the solid oak blocks must be worth a mint.

Lunch time is over and as I enter the ward day room I see that King Smith has arrived and is sitting on the sofa by the window. He looks completely zombiefied. Up to the eyebrows with medication. As I approach him I look directly into his face. His eyes have a far away look that says there's no one in, no one's at home. The rest of the day is again spent tearing up these bloody packets. It's now hinted by some staff that this is more than just an ego struggle between two competing charge nurses. It's rumoured that there's a promotion in the offing as head of industrial therapy but it's the patients and staff here that are doing the graft not Bob. Most of the time he just sits in his office for hours on end reading or talking on the phone. Occasionally he comes out to survey the progress that is being made before returning to the comfort of his office. All he lacks is a whip and jackboots.

Today some new clothing stocks have arrived on the ward. The usual standard rough wool socks, sackcloth like shirts and awful thick woollen ties have been replaced with nylon socks, fine cotton shirts with modern collars and rayon ties.. They are all in a variety of modern colours and patterns. My guess is that some of these new clothes are going to stimulate the staff's long loan system but it's also nice to know that there will be improvements in the appearance and comfort of the patients.

Thank goodness my last duty day has arrived and I will soon escape from this industrial drudgery. This morning I am out working in the garden with two staff and a small group of patients. King Smith is one of them. He is completely retarded by the drugs he is being given and unable to do any work in his present condition. However it's a lovely sunny day and the rest of us are enjoying the benefit of being out in the fresh air. We have got the task of tidying the flower beds and have obtained all the necessary equipment, forks, spades and hoes. I am particularly enjoying the freedom and the exercise. If I feel pleased to be outdoors how do the patients feel? I'm not sure, you can never tell! It's 11 am and we stop for a cup of tea. King Smith has been going through the motions of tickling the soil with his shovel. As we stand around in a bunch, drinking, some patients are resting on their shovels and patients lucky enough to possess a fag or dog end are having a smoke. King Smith is standing to the front of me just behind one of the staff nurses. He slowly starts to lift his shovel, it's going up very deliberately and I see immediately what his intention is. He's going to hit the staff nurse over the head. A few quick strides and I am at his side and reach up and grab the shovel. I have no difficulty wresting it from his grasp, as he is very weak as well as very slow. The staff nurse half turns with a slightly perplexed look on his face then realises what's been going on. He looks at me and says "Thanks for that, I didn't see it coming". So now I know that there is someone at home inside King Smith's head. He gives the impression of being a zombie but it's now apparent that he knows what's going on around him and is capable of deciding what he wants to do. In this job I am beginning to understand that unpredictability is the only predictable aspect of this type of work.

The rest of the shift passes without incident and as I watch more evening dirge on TV I drift off "out of the window," thinking about the consequences of leaving behind my cousin Michael and this vulnerable group of patients. For the future it doesn't really matter how many good nurses pass in and out of this ward. It's not until Bob and his henchmen are moved from here that that there will be a chance of changing things for the better. However the likelihood even then is that nothing will change for I am sure that there is no shortage of aggressive bastards to replace them. Anyway there's no real prospect of moving Bob. It's well known that he likes it here, this is his roost and the managers are afraid of his Union power and will not want to upset him. Bob is destined to continue his ill-treatment of patients with impunity. When I am gone Michael will almost certainly be on the receiving end of some "thump therapy" once again and realistically I know that there is not a damn thing that can be done about it.

Over the last few months I have established a fairly close group of good like minded friends, some of whom will be with me in school this Monday. They are a strange mix. There is bearded Bill with one fixed knee joint, he is an ardent Communist who has written for Pravda, Vince my special pal, the dark brown African, Dan Sing an affable Sikh who Jim calls Dan-Sing in the Dark, John a homosexual Jehovah's Witness, David a would be Baptist Minister and of course Jim the joker. Jim gives pet names to anyone who has any distinguishing features or unusual personality traits. One student not known for his cheerfulness Jim calls the depressed pest or his little ray of misery. Another who has a rather large head he calls the Mekon because of his resemblance to the green space alien in the Marvel Comic. He has now invented a nickname for me, its Manic Mac. I suppose if the cap fits I have to wear it. I do recognise that I have a marked tendency to get involved in anything and everything and then I tire very quickly and move on to something else.

The news has just reached me that one of my friends wives has had a baby boy and it has as I feared turned out the be Vince's. She had left her husband before the birth and they were getting a divorce. Vince has agreed with her to take the boy and bring him up on his own. As she already has two young children I think this may be the best solution and I feel sure Vince will make a very fine father.

CHAPTER 3.

LEARNING & EARNING

It was with a certain amount of trepidation that I contemplated going into the nurse training school on the first occasion as I have never really enjoyed or excelled in schools of any type and I went to six during my childhood. However my attitude to learning has changed dramatically since my first encounter in the nurse training school with our senior tutor John Winkley. Up to this point I had never met anyone that I could really admire for their personality, philosophy and depth of knowledge. He opened a whole new world for me. The world of anatomy, physiology, psychology, the idea's of Freud, Adler and Yung and practical nursing. His lectures were spell-binding and packed with pure information.. So I am looking forward to my second six week period in school with a sense of excitement and anticipation.

As I enter the classroom on the first day I see that a number of nurses have already arrived. Jimmy the skeleton is still hanging forlornly on his stand in his usual place near the window. The room is like any old fashioned school classroom, wood floorboards, oak panelling, two blackboards and rows of wooden desks with lids and bench seats. I greet my colleagues with a cheery Hi as the room steadily fills up with chattering male and female nurses. There are some good lookers amongst the females so I have to remember that I fairly recently married one of my previous class mates. As 9am approaches we all dutifully sit down at our desks. Then the room goes quiet as we hear footsteps along the wood floored corridor and seconds later John Winkley enters in his characteristic manner. Everyone I have ever spoken to in the hospital has an enormous respect for him and a degree of reverence that you can almost feel. He has a tendency to stoop slightly and initially look down when he enters the room. He is dressed in an immaculate white coat. His height is about average and he is of sinuous asthenic build. His skin has an unusual brownish, yellow tinge rather like parchment. His mop of frizzy fine brown hair looks almost afro. His lips are well defined and he usually has an intense if not slightly pained expression on his face. His voice is low and gravelly. We all remain silent in anticipation until he speaks. I'm far from academically inclined and therefore not a great one for studying but during his lectures I hang on to every word that he utters and amazingly they sink in. I could sit and listen to him for hours. Because of my level of intense concentration it seems that no sooner has he started his lecture on the anatomy and physiology of the kidneys that I hear him utter the words "coffee break"; I really have been so engrossed that I haven't noticed an hour and a half fly by. This is very different from when I worked in a factory; then I would watch the movement of the clock's minute hand until the final whistle blew at 5pm. Then I was first out of the gate on my bike pedalling like hell until I got home.

The rest of the morning passes just as quickly and it's now off to lunch. Jim is already at a table and having got my lunch I sit down beside him. As I do he excitedly waves the hospital magazine in my face. "Have you seen this"? Jim shows me an item that reads" Is the male nurse who tried to climb into a female nurse's first floor window of the Nurses Home still smarting from the bruises he received when she pushed him off the window ledge into the laurel bushes below. "With a mischievous and secretive smile Jim says, guess who? I am intrigued but I haven't a clue. "It was Frank Smith" he says with obvious glee. "Do you know who the female nurse was?" Again I have to say that I have no idea. Jim laughs and says "It was big Maggie" Well that certainly takes the biscuit. Frank is a student who is said to like a drink, so if he was inebriated I can believe he might have made the fatal error of scaling the Nurses Home drainpipe with amorous intentions. But boy oh boy didn't he pick the wrong window. Maggie is a big girl with a big personality and obviously she has an equally big push. Poor Frank was lucky in two ways. His first bit of luck was that she didn't drag him into her room with equally amorous intent and the second was that he didn't break his neck when he fell.

Jim is a mine of information and salacious stories. His second piece of less startling news is that Bob Russell of the big sausage incident has gone onto permanent night duty. I feel almost sure that he has gone on nights to escape the constant innuendo and teasing from staff who should know better. The last piece of news is tragic. Two elderly long stay patients have suffocated in one of the ground floor ward boot rooms. Apparently they were sitting in the boot room when they were overcome by smoke coming through the window from the burning oak blocks just outside the building. I ask Jim if he knows who they were but he doesn't. I know if they were sitting in the boot room they would certainly have been allowed to wander the corridors and grounds so I would have known them by sight if not by name.

Back in school in the Practical Room we are being taught to give injections. I have heard that in other schools they practice on oranges but no such luck here, John Winkley has told us each to draw up a syringe of sterile water and inject each other in the upper arms. I have chosen one of the females to give me mine, I hope she will be gentle with me. No need to worry, I don't even feel the needle going in but I speak too soon, she presses the plunger down as if she's blowing up bicycle tyres and boy do I jump. Seeing me wince on her second attempt she is more gentle; she slowly presses the plunger with great care and I don't feel a thing. When I return the favour I feel how soft and delicate the skin is on her upper arm and determine not to hurt her. As a result I have no problem giving her two injections, there's not even the slightest flinch or a murmur from her. I feel chuffed to bits.

After the injection session the tutor asks us to gather around the demonstration bed that has a full sized anatomically realistic female doll in it. We all eagerly surround the bed and watch intently as John Winkley demonstrates how to pass a naso-gastric tube into the stomach. Out of the side of my eye I notice one of the female nurses called Mary, a tall slim mischievous blonde. She is circling furtively around the back of the group towards me. Now she's edging closer, she is right behind me and I can now feel her breath on the back of my neck. What's she up to? Suddenly I feel her hand sliding in through the side vent of my white coat. It searches for a moment then slips into my trouser pocket. She then starts to fondle what she shouldn't be fondling. She's like this all the time with the male nurses. She's a lovely girl, bright, full of fun but she has absolutely no inhibitions and has gained a reputation of being bit of a goer. It's excruciating to feel her fiddling around while I am trying to remain calm and concentrate on the demonstration. I don't want to cause an embarrassing situation so instinctively I gently get hold of her wrist but as I do I realise that if I trap her hand in my pocket it could be there even longer, so I let go. After a short while her curiosity is obviously satisfied and she withdraws her hand and moves away along the back of the group towards the next unsuspecting object of her curiosity or desire.

The rest of the afternoon passes as quickly as the morning did and before we know it it's afternoon tea break. As we saunter down the corridor towards the staff cafe Mary leans towards me as she passes, she smiles mischievously and says less than coyly "Did you enjoy that?" With a bit of bravado I grin and reply "another place another time Mary".

Back from break we all gather in the Group Room at the end of the corridor. This is where we have free floating discussions with the tutors. As I take a seat in the circle of chairs my eyes alight on a student opposite me, his shirt and tie look very familiar. My eyes travel down towards his socks, then move on to the next student's shirt, tie and socks, they too look familiar. Then to the next student and the next. That clinches it, most of them are wearing the new clothes provided for the patients. No hanging about here; they have all cottoned on to the same idea and have quickly taken advantage of the hospital's unofficial long loan system. John Winkley entering the room breaks my train of thought and he begins a discussion about whether or not we would be happy to be admitted to this hospital as a patient. When it comes to my turn I say I would if I could choose to be admitted to the Collingwood Clinic but not the main hospital. I then quickly qualify this by saying I would not want to be a patient in any ward including the clinic if I was very disturbed or aggressive. Interestingly nobody takes up either of these points or even asks the question why. It's another case of the three wise monkeys. Hear no evil, speak no evil, see no evil.

It's the next day and unfortunately we are booked to have lectures from the other tutor Tommy Hindmarsh. He's a strange looking character, tall and slim and as bald as a coot. He has a rather white face and a maniacal expression. You could imagine he would be easy to make up to look like Coco the clown. He is a nice pleasant man who is obviously keen and enthusiastic about the subjects he teaches but he just cannot project his enthusiasm or keenness to us. He is a dreadful lecturer and drones on and on. I totally lose interest after a while and I couldn't tell you what he has been on about for the last half hour. I find myself looking at Jimmy the skeleton hanging in the corner of the room, or is it Jemima. Some say the skeleton is that of a woman. I wonder about the type of life it led, about its family. I'm sure that whoever it was never expected to end up hanging in a hospital classroom; it seems so undignified. Suddenly I am awakened from my day dreams by the tutor announcing loudly that tomorrow we are visiting the hospital mortuary to see a post mortem. The announcement brings us all quickly to life with a buzz of excitement. I have laid out lots of dead patients in the last 18 months but the thought of seeing a post mortem is still quite daunting. I know that this is going to be a macabre and grizzly experience but we all appear to be looking forward to the event even if it is with a mixture of excitement, dread and anxiety, such is human nature. It's strange how even the most gentle and benign of human beings are fascinated by morbid subjects such as death, mutilation, pain and suffering. I have recognised this in my own reactions to the ill-treatment and death of patients. Alongside the feelings of repugnance, pity and anger that I had fully expected to feel are much less comfortable feelings of fascination and excitement. Coming to terms with this dark side of my nature is a relatively new and psychologically challenging experience. As we walk away from the school I meet Jim in the corridor and mention to him yesterday's observation of male students wearing patient's clothes. He chuckles, leans forward towards me and pulls out his tie from his pullover. I see that as usual he is already one step ahead of the game. He is wearing one of the new ties but he has cut the bottom third off that has the hospital stamp on it and thrown it away. He's as wily as a fox. It would be a great system if it wasn't dishonest. First you borrow the hospital's property then when it's dirty you return it to the ward and then you borrow another one. No need to buy shirts, ties or socks, no personal laundering involved and as the theory goes it's not theft either. The same system operates for hospital sheets, pillowcases and towels.

Day three and there's a feeling of anticipation as I arrive in class this morning. The chatter level is high and everyone seems very animated. Much of the conversation is about to-day's impending visit to the mortuary. Suddenly the door opens and John Winkley walks in carrying a white enamel bucket. He asks us all to gather round and as I push forward I wonder what's coming next. He removes the bucket lid and I see two brains sloshing around the bottom of the bucket in some blood stained clear fluid. The smell is putrid and we all step back out of range. The tutor explains that these are the brains of the two old patients who suffocated in the boot room a few days ago. He informs us that the reason for showing us this unedifying sight is that they died from carbon monoxide poisoning. This gives the blood vessels in the brain a characteristic bright pink colour and also turns the brain tissue into an almost jelly-like substance. Personally I would be happier just to have this explained to me or to have been shown photographs. These two old boys were alive walking the corridors just a few days ago. Now how can anyone know which brain belongs to which patient? Obviously its now impossible to tell, which leads me to wonder how these brains are going to be put back in the right body? Another thought is; will they be put back at all, somehow I doubt it. We are taught to preserve the dignity of a dead patient when we are laying them out in preparation for their journey to the mortuary. This spectacle is inconsistent with that teaching but then many situations in this hospital are inconsistent. To me even the very name hospital seems incongruous and misleading.

At eleven o'clock we are marshalled together to proceed down the drive to the mortuary. On the way there I notice that cigarettes are being brought out and there's a definite lull in the chatter; to me this is a sure sign of apprehension. As we turn off down a narrow bush lined path I see that it's leading to a dingy looking building. Ahead there is an open door leading into a dark interior. As we file through the door the stench hits us, it smells like a combination of a wet fish shop and a butcher's. I immediately minimise the smell by starting to breath through my mouth. On a slab in front of me is the pale yellowish naked body of an emaciated old man. His head is resting on a wooden block and his sightless eyes are staring up towards the ceiling. His penis is tightly tied in a bow with a soiled piece of bandage and a label is similarly attached to his big toe. The tutor gestures to us to gather around the slab and we all cautiously shuffle forward, not anxious to get too near. The tutor then introduces the doctor who is going to perform the autopsy. He is a small fat rosy cheeked man with a podgy but impassive face. He is dressed in a rather soiled extremely long white coat several sizes too big for him. He starts by showing us his array of carpentry tools hanging on the walls and on a narrow bench beside him. There are drills, saws, hammers, cutters and an array of lethal looking knives of all shapes and sizes. On the bench there is a number of round kidney shaped enamel bowls and a large weighing machine with brass weights. This place is just a butcher's shop with a difference. The meat is human. We wait in silence for the gory show to begin. The doctor takes a scalpel in his hand and draws it deftly down the old mans abdomen from his sternum to his pubis, his belly peels open like a burst paper bag. God! The smell is now really overpowering as he lifts the stomach and intestines out to examine them. I don't feel all that brilliant so to reassure myself I look to see how my colleagues are coping. Some have put hankies over their mouths and noses. Others have gone rather grey and are swaying. I hope this is going to be over soon. The doctor then cuts the liver free and pulls it out, placing it on the scales. Next he takes this large dark red soggy blob of flesh off the scales, places it on the bench and starts to slice it up and examine it. He then passes it around for us to handle. It's like holding a piece of black currant jelly. Honest to God I will never eat liver again or anything else that looks remotely anatomical. The doctor then reaches for a cutter and starts to hack his way through the old man's rib cage. This is a step too far for some of the nurses and they indicate that they must leave. The tutor responds by nodding towards the door and they almost fall over each other to make a hasty exit. Next the heart and lungs are removed, weighed, sliced open and dissected. I am now feeling quite nauseated but am determined to see it through to the bitter end. The doctor then moves towards the old man's head and runs the scalpel from round the back of the neck up to the left and right temples. He then grasps the loosened skin at the back of the neck and tears the scalp off pulling it over the patient's face with the hair on the inside. To hold the retracted scalp in place he stretches the skin over and under the old mans chin. The sight of the patient's face protruding though the inside of his own scalp is horrendous and momentarily I instinctively turn away. Then the drilling begins accompanied by the smell of burning flesh and bone. Next a saw is used to completely remove the top of the skull. It's like taking the top off a soft boiled egg. The doctor then reaches down inside the skull, and cuts the brain away from the spinal cord and eyes and scoops it out, leaving me peering inside the patient's empty skull. At this point I look intently at the doctor's impassive face and wonder why anyone would want to do this job for a living even on a part time basis? How can they do this and live a near normal life? Does it change their view of people? Do they eye up their friends as potential cadavers? Sure it's a part of reality but thank goodness it is a part of reality that most people will never have to face. My thoughts are broken by the person next to me passing me a part of brain to examine and I quickly pass it on. It's like the game pass the parcel, everyone is eager to pass it on as quickly as possible. Once it's done the rounds the tutor announces that the viewing is finished. He thanks the doctor and I mutter thank goodness under my breath as I quickly file out of the door with the others. As I hit the outside I take a huge gulp of cool beautiful fresh air and clear my nose, mouth and lungs. Never again! As I walk up the drive my colleagues are still rather subdued. I wonder why this is a necessary part of the training syllabus. My view as a trainee psychiatric nurse is that this awful experience is of no real value. Why can't we just make do with the anatomical models in the school; with these we can see each organ and its place in the body and we can remove and replace them. Surely that's enough for our particular type of training. There is also Jimmy the skeleton to help us study the skeletal system. As we get back to the classroom the conversation lifts slightly but still revolves mainly around what we have just seen. I gather up my belongings and decide

I have no stomach for lunch.

We are now in our last week in school and the time has passed quickly. We had been asked to write a short essay on what the future of the hospital should be. Since I handed my paper in for marking I've been waiting to get it back. I'm curious to see if there is any reaction to what I have written and also to see how many marks I have received. In particular I am interested to see if there is a reaction to a contentious statement I made at the end of my essay. I had written that as soon as possible the hospital should be razed to the ground and the staff should be scattered to the four winds. Not the sort of statement that is easy to ignore but I sense it is being ignored and I think I know why.

The rest of the week passes quickly and today is our last day. John Winkley has re-affirmed all the ideals I hold dear but dare not speak openly about, other than to close friends who share my opinions. One day maybe in the distant future, they will be more generally accepted. I have still had no response to my essay, mind you, nobody else has either, maybe the papers are just filed as examples of our work. As a parting gesture on this our last afternoon John Winkley has given us a poem by John Clare who lived in the 19th century and who spent the last 22 years of his life as a patient in Northampton County Asylum. For me this poem conveys all the isolation, sense of loss and unhappiness that I imagine many patients experience but may not be able to articulate. I vow in the next few days to memorise it. So here goes!

AN OBLIVIOUS HOST

I am yet who I am, who cares or knows
my friends forsake me as a memory lost
I am the self-consumer of my woes
they rise and vanish an oblivious host
Shadows of life who's very soul is lost
and yet I am, I live though I am tossed

Into the nothingness of scorn and noise
Into the living sea of waking dreams
Where there is neither sense of life nor joys
but the huge shipwreck of my own esteem
and all that's dear, even those I loved the best
are strange, nay they are stranger than the rest

I long for scenes where never man has trod
For scenes where woman never smiled nor wept
There to abide with my creator God
and sleep as in childhood sweetly slept
Full of high thoughts unborn, so let me die
The grass below, above, the vaulted sky.

John Clare 1864

CHAPTER 4.

UNUSUAL EVENTS

Months have now passed since I was in school. It has been an eventful time. I have passed my intermediate examination and received the standard £40 bonus for doing so. Combined with my weekly pay this is a lot of money but unfortunately it has all been spent on paying bills. Now that my wife and I have blown it all we are back on Skid Row trying to eke out a living on my meagre pay. The only way we survive is by my working every day of my three or four days off. The week before last I even did two jobs together, my normal job at the hospital during the day and looking after an old man in his own house during the night. He was a rich Jewish gentleman who owned a tailoring business. We got on so well that he had promised me a world tour when he got better. Unfortunately he did not survive. I was not bothered about losing the world tour, I took that with a pinch of salt; my regret was about not being able to help save such a nice old man. When his end came I had worked continuously for three days and three nights with almost no sleep. When I finally got home to bed I slept for two days and two nights solid. Never again!

During these last few months I have also worked on two very interesting wards. First on the sick ward, then the Collingwood Clinic. For almost the first time since I started work here I have seen good care as it should be delivered consistently and collectively by all the nurses. On my entry to the sick ward on my first morning I was greeted by an old man staggering towards me with his hand outstretched "I am John Pigg but I am no relative of that Hog over there." He gestured towards another old man who sat in the corner. He explained later that the other old man was called Bill Hogg. This was a rare occasion, a joke coming from a patient; in fact I don't think I had ever heard a patient make a joke, but considering their circumstances I can fully understand why.

Some breakfast times on this ward were a sight to behold. The charge nurse Jimmy Heron was enormous, he must have weighed well over 20 stone. He would stagger in at 7.30 am with his shoe laces undone, his collar open with his tie draped around his neck. He would ease himself down in the only chair that could accept his huge frame and support his colossal weight. After helping himself to an enormous bacon sandwich, dripping with fat, from the patient's breakfast trolley he would launch himself at it with fat oozing out of his mouth and running down his chin and over his hands. Not a very edifying sight. One of the well trained worker patients would then appear and start tying Jimmy's shoe laces and putting on his tie. Then to top this spectacle the charge nurse would get the patient to bring his violin from the clinical room and then proceed to treat us all to a markedly less than virtuoso performance. To say this scene was rather bizarre for a hospital sick ward is to understate the case. However Jimmy Heron was a very good nurse with qualifications in psychiatry and general nursing and he ran an excellent ward.

Another notable nurse was a small dapper deputy charge nurse called Frank Kavanah who was possibly in his early fifties. He confided to me one day that at the start of his career he had been one of the so called hard men who participated in beating up patients. However he had since realised through his Catholic religion that he was in the wrong. I admired him both for his honesty and for his bravery. There are not too many people who can fully acknowledge their past mistakes and change their ways for the better. I have some understanding of just how easy it is to move from being a carer to becoming an abuser of patients. I have witnessed a number of fellow students who have very quickly gone down this path. However Frank is now a brilliant nurse who is 100 percent dedicated to helping patients. Another lovely character and wonderful nurse on this ward was Avro Grikitas. He was Estonian or Latvian, I'm not sure which, but he treated all the patients with great care and affection. He was also a brilliant gymnast which he demonstrated by hand walking on the floor then mounting a chair and from there mounting and balancing on a table. Not only did this require balancing ability but also considerable strength.

Shaving patients was a daily chore that I didn't particularly relish because the cheap razor blades that were issued were almost useless, particularly after shaving several patients with days of stubble on their faces. The difficult part was shaving people under their noses or under their double chins. Not exactly my best idea for whiling away an hour or two. On one morning I was given the job of shaving a new bedridden patient. As I approached his bed there was something about him that gave me a strange creepy feeling. He was emaciated and his pyjama jacket hung off his body. It was buttonless and gaped open at the front exposing his pale skin stretched over a bony ribcage. He had a long angular yellowy white face with high cheek bones. His protruding uneven rotten teeth were barely contained within his well defined pale lips. He didn't show any acknowledgement when I said I was going to give him a shave. There was not even a twitch of a facial muscle and his pale watery eyes stared unblinkingly ahead as if he was in a trance. To the touch his skin was cold and slightly greasy. Not a word passed between us as I shaved him but I had a strange feeling that his mind was fully alive and seething with some form of evil. I don't use the word evil often but I cannot describe my feelings in any other terms. Once the job was done I forgot about him and went on to shave the other patients. Three months later I picked up an evening paper and from the front page I saw a photograph of a face staring out at me under a headline "Man found guilty of boy's murder." I was sure I recognised the face but where from? I still couldn't bring the face to mind. When I read the article below and saw the words "previously a patient in St. Nicholas Hospital" it dawned on me. Its was him, the guy I shaved in the sick ward. The article went on to say that the body of a young boy had been found under the boxing ring at St James's Park Boxing Hall in Newcastle. The boy had some association with the man who was employed as a cleaner at the hall. The boy's body had been cut into four pieces and secreted under the boxing ring but the smell of it decomposing had led to its discovery. This ex patient was I believe sentenced to life imprisonment . One thing I was proud of during my time on this ward was assisting in the recovery of a young man who had been involved in a serious road traffic accident. His head injury was so bad that surgeons had to remove half the frontal lobe of his brain, about a cup full. They had also removed half of the front of his scull and eye socket. He looked horrendous with half his forehead set back half an inch, with his left eye fallen out of line with the right.

His jaw had also been broken and to hold it in place

his top and lower jaw had been wired together. This made feeding him very difficult and the danger of him choking made the process even more hazardous. Because of his severe brain injury he continuously omitted a high pitched animal like scream. He did this none stop night and day. The trained nurses told me that the scream was identical with the scream of someone with meningitis. As he was emaciated I fed him with my own special liquid concoction. It was comprised of 2 pints of milk, 4 raw eggs, 4 ounces of powdered food supplements, Complan and Casilan, together with a few tablespoons of Horlicks and Glucose. He loved it and woofed it down. Because his jaw was wired together we used to push chocolate drops between his teeth. Gradually he gained weight and his cries became less frequent. After several weeks he started to show considerable improvement. One day I sensed that he was beginning to recover some of his mental capacity and although he couldn't talk his eyes seemed to follow me as I passed his bed. My curiosity aroused, I got a pen and paper and went and sat by his bed. Putting the pad in front of him and the pen in his hand I said "write your name". In response he gave one of his screams which suggested to me he didn't want to participate but I persisted, "write your name" This time he moved his hand in a very shaky put purposeful way. At this moment I realised he was aware of what I was saying and it had registered what I wanted him to do. The pen moved slowly across the paper and there scrawled in spider like lettering was his first name. I was thrilled. This signature was the first evidence that we had seen that he was on the road to at least a partial recovery. Only time would tell how good the recovery would be. Many months later, after his discharge I saw him coming up the hospital drive with his mother, looking like something from a horror movie and I wondered if it wouldn't have been kinder if he had died. I understood that the purpose of this ward is to treat the sick but occasionally I wondered why patients like him and John Pigg and Bill Hogg were admitted to a psychiatric hospital when their predominant signs and symptoms were physical. Another such patient that I had doubts about was the Ex Curator of the Hancock Industrial Museum in central Newcastle. He had undergone surgery for the removal of a brain tumour. Seeing this tall dignified man standing naked in a cold bathroom corridor waiting in line with other naked patients for a bath seemed wrong and totally unnecessary.

During this period I also worked on the Collingwood Clinic, an admission ward that was opened in 1956 for patients with acute psychiatric conditions. This included an Electro Convulsive Therapy (ECT) Department. Patients were transported down by ambulance from the main hospital three times a week for this treatment. The ward was staffed by highly experienced dually qualified nurses under an older charge nurse called Arthur Howe. He was a very good nurse but a bit of a ditherer who seemed preoccupied most of the time but he was also very methodical and careful. Someone on the ward with access to the ward keys must have been watching him closely and noting his daily routine. They must have noticed that Arthur always kept about ten new patients suits in reserve for emergency use. He kept them in a locked cupboard opposite the padded cell. And every day when he was on duty he would count the suits to ensure that all ten were there. On one particular day I accompanied him to get some soap which he also kept locked in the cupboard. While I was waiting behind him in the corridor he started to count the suit jackets on the rail. For some reason he broke with his usual practice and took one down to look inside the jacket. To his surprise and consternation the trousers were missing. So he opened another suit, and again no trousers and then the next suit and the next. Four pairs of trousers were missing, I presumed stolen. As it had always been his practice to count only the jackets he had no way of knowing when the trousers had gone, it could have been weeks or even months ago and for that reason he wouldn't be able to track down the culprit. One thing was for sure. To have access to the keys to the cupboard it must have been a trained nurse, most possibly one on night duty. It's easier to steal at night and get stolen goods out of the door and into your car boot. I had to smile to myself, there are some very wily and unscrupulous buggers in this place.

While I was working at this Clinic I came across some treatments that I had only heard or read about. They were Continual Narcosis and Insulin Coma Therapy. It appears that these treatments are potentially dangerous. Luckily they are on their way to becoming obsolete. It amazes me that some leading psychiatrists have made huge reputations and a good living lecturing and writing books about these and other forms of treatment such as electric shock for alcoholics. and homosexuals, when ultimately the supporting evidence turns out to be without foundation and the treatments themselves are found to be ineffective. When they are giving their academic lectures about these treatments even fellow doctors appear to hang on to every word as if their words and idea's are sacrosanct and irrefutable.

We received some sad news on the hospital bush telegraph today. Bob Russell, the staff nurse has committed suicide. It has not been announced officially and I have no details but it may be that he took an overdose. I knew instinctively when I saw that incident with the sausage in the staff dining room that he was masking acute embarrassment. I also felt that him going on nights was an attempt to escape from the ridicule, or even an attempt to escape from his own inner conflict as a Roman

Catholic. It's very sad because he was a marvellous nurse and a lovely person but he was also possibly too sensitive. If only those who tease or belittle other people reflected more on their behaviour and the possible outcomes.

Another near tragic event happened on an ECT day. The ambulance was making its usual short trip from the main hospital just across the road. In it were about six patients and a male escort and the driver. As they got halfway down the drive one of the patients grabbed the ambulance driver from behind, pulled his head back and slit his throat with a hacksaw blade. Luckily what saved the driver was having his head pulled back. In this position the vital arteries move deeper into the back of the neck and provide slightly more protection from serious injury. Anyway the driver survived and there were no other casualties. The patient was transferred to a more secure ward and more stringent safety measures were introduced for transporting patients.

One other memorable event occurred one morning when I went to the Women's Institute mobile trolley for a bar of chocolate. Two new woman patients still in their hospital dressing gowns had beaten me to it. One was being served when the other woman said to her "what are you in here for?" The woman turned to her and with a deadpan expression said "I shot my husband with a rifle" I expected a reaction of shock and silence but the woman retorted "Where did you get the courage from, I've always wanted to shoot mine." I immediately realised that I had read of her trial in the papers several months ago. Apparently her husband was in the army and she herself was a crack shot and had competed at Bisley shooting tournament. It appeared that during an argument she had shot her husband in the chest at point blank range with his own rifle. The judge at the trial said he didn't believe that she had intended to kill him because as a markswoman at that range she would have shot him through the heart. I remember having doubts about the judge's opinion because she fired from the hip not the shoulder. This method of shooting with a rifle is unusual and even at close range is not that accurate.

Two other stomach churning events occurred during this time. The first took place on the female side of the hospital when a condom was found at lunch time at the bottom of a large tin of hot stewed apple. The worst thing was that it was not until all the female patients had finished their pudding of apple and custard that the condom was discovered. Apparently the offending item was held out between finger and thumb and taken to the Matrons Office as evidence of a serious misdemeanour. Another similar event occurred when a used condom was found by a very meticulous charge nurse in the pocket of his clean white coat that he always hung inside his office door.

It could be that it was the same perpetrator and that he or she was a member of staff. What the motivation for perpetrating these dreadful acts was one can only guess but I have no doubt it was the product of a very nasty mind.

CHAPTER 5.

BETTS BUDGIES

I have just come back from the usual melee around the main corridor change list. This time I'm quite pleased to see that tomorrow I will be working for the next six weeks on Ward 16 and better still, Jim is warded there with me. Both of us have been on the ward before for a short period. Jim has named the ward Betts Budgies, Betts comes from the name of the charge nurse George Betts and the budgies from Jim's characterisation of the patients. With the exception of the very elderly they are the most deteriorated long stay patients in the hospital. Very few are capable of doing even menial work outside the ward in other departments of the hospital or its grounds.

It's not a good start on this my first shift. Thanks to the lousy bus service I am late for duty. I have run the full length of the main drive to arrive sweating at the bottom of the stairs to the main ward door. I take the stairs three at a time and breathlessly come to a halt in front of the ward's solid wood door. Brilliant, I have forgotten my keys, something I never do. This is definitely not my day. I start banging heavily on the door but there's no response. I consider kicking it but check myself, Its not a good way of gaining entrance on my first day. So I start banging and banging and banging again. Suddenly I hear the sound of footsteps and the jingling of keys. The lock turns and the door opens, revealing a small thickset man in a white coat. I haven't seen him before but my instant first impressions are not good. "Come in" he says with a lisp or a lilt or both. He sounds Irish but it's his shifty look and something about his manner that are off-putting. As I step into the ward another door opens to my right and a second thickset figure emerges. My new found colleague addresses him and says "this is the new student." He responds in a deep gruff voice "They don't teach you the time in school then! Show him where to hang his coat and get him back down here sharpish, I haven't got all bloody day."

As we walk through the dining room my new colleague introduces himself as Sean and tells me he is a State Enrolled Nurse (SEN), one grade lower than a State Registered Nurse. He informs me that George Betts was moved at the time of the change list and his replacement is Charge Nurse Larry Docherty. He says he's a tough old nut but OK if you keep on the right side of him. It's a pity George Betts has left as Jim and I found him to be one of a group of benign and friendly charge nurses who treated patients well. He was a true gentleman. I give Jim a wave as I see him coming out of the dormitory escorting two patients into the toilets. I hasten back to the charge nurse's office and tell him I have left my keys at home. He pulls a face as if to say another useless bugger, opens a drawer in his desk and without a word slaps a key on the desk in front of me. I get the message loud and clear. Not long ago misplacing or losing a ward key meant instant dismissal.

The rows of dark brown topped Formica tables have been set for breakfast. Sean has informed me that the tables are set out in rows with the most able patients nearest the kitchen serving hatch and the least able at the opposite end. Once the time honoured practice of one nurse saying grace is over I can see why the tables are set as they are. Near the service hatch the more able patients are eating reasonably sedately and would not disgrace themselves in a trucker's café. At the other end it's like a rugby scrum with each patient trying to outdo the others by cramming in as much food and tea into his mouth in the shortest possible time whilst guarding his own plate from pilferers with an eagle eye and both arms around the plate. Knives and forks sit unused on the table while arms and hands flail everywhere. Food that misses the hungry mouths is splattered on the table, floor and down the patient's ties and jacket lapels. Soon the table is cleared of every vestige of food and the tea pot is emptied in two minutes flat.

After breakfast I team up with Jim. He had gone into the backs and re-emerges with two wet towels, one of which he throws at me. Chuckling he says "Operation mop up, give me a hand." We approach the top table where the ducks are still sitting. Jim has renamed them. They are no longer Betts Budgies they are now Docherty's Ducks. Although this sounds demeaning and derogatory I am sure it's not intended this way. It's just part of Jim's black humour to lighten the day. If you didn't have a sense of humour the endless routine and boredom could drive you mad. Certainly Jim's attitude and behaviour towards these long stay chronic patients is beyond fault. The patients are still sitting at the table like young fledglings waiting for their mother to return with more food. We begin to mop down the caked on food from their jacket lapels, ties and trouser fronts. Some parts of their misshapen coarse wool suits are impregnated with what appears to be several days of what could be described as swill. All of them would make scarecrows look well dressed.

For reasons of cost and hygiene patient's suits are not dry cleaned but boiled to ensure that caked on food, urine, nose dropping and excrement are adequately dealt with. The overall effect on the suits is devastating, the jackets and trousers quickly shrink and the shoulder padding becomes lumpy and out of place. Added to this patients often fasten their jacket and trouser buttons out of sequence, to say nothing of their ties that resemble knotted rags and their shoes with their trodden down heels and untied laces which flop up and down as the walk. Their hair is sometimes shaven in basin cut fashion with numerous bald patches that makes their heads look like dishevelled coconuts. All of this gives the patients their characteristic appearance and gait, that would be easily recognisable a hundred yards away even through the wrong end of a pair of binoculars.

Larry Docherty emerges from the office and strides towards us. In his hand he is clutching a fist full of cigarettes. The patients quickly gather round as he shouts out several names. Charlie, John, William. He then throws the cigarettes towards them and they deftly catch them and quickly turn and walk away. The remaining group mill around in anticipation as he throws the cigarettes one by one into the air. A mad scramble breaks out as they fight to get the cigarettes. It's like a rugby scrum. Some patients are successful in retaining a cigarette or a piece of one for a second before it is snatched out of their hand or mouth by another patient. Larry laughs gruffly at the sight of this undignified spectacle, he obviously enjoys this so called game. Some patients who are successful in picking up a few pieces are chased up the ward by two or three patients determined to wrest them from them. Having expended all the cigarettes and grown tired of the spectacle Larry retreats into his office. A few minutes later he emerges again this time with a few razor blades in his hand. He instructs Jim and me to "Get them in the backs and give them a shave." He starts to round them up for us, pulling some out of their chairs and forcibly propelling them towards the door. Some get a smack on the back of their head while others get a kick up the backside accompanied by a few none too polite words to encourage them on their way.

Inside the bathroom it's like Siberia with the white tiled walls adding nothing to convey warmth. Four white enamel cups half full with cold soggy soap are on the window sill. The five razor blades we have been given are of the cheap non branded variety. We have about thirty patients to shave with three days growth on their faces, some have tough stubble that resembles wire wool. The first to be selected for this unique form of torture is a patient called Charlie Bates or Master Bates as he is known colloquially because of his nocturnal activities. He is completely round the twist. He stands in front of me typifying the universal face of madness. His face is deathly white with an unruly mop of black hair sprouting out at every angle. He has a permanent maniacal grin and incessantly talks gibberish. He looks at me and says in a Geordie dialect "That little laddie doon the street. See ya got a little no hinny, you know little Timmy then" as if I understood every word. He has the usual burnt nose, lips and tongue from smoking dog ends and rolled up paper. Shaving him is a nightmare as he keeps turning his face from side to side. When I have finished, his face above his lips and his chin are covered with bits of toilet paper to stem the blood from numerous minor cuts. Jim looks at my handiwork and chuckles "Christ Mac he looks as if he has been in a massacre."

We have shaved about fifteen patients now with five blades and they are so blunt you couldn't cut butter with them. It's sheer agony for the patients and totally unnecessary. What we need is one decent blade for two to three patients; but what we are allowed is one cheap blade for every eight patients. Jim has been trying to re-sharpen them on the window glass. He says it works but I have my doubts and if anything I think it makes them more blunt.

My old friend Psyche is next, he has been transferred here from Ward 20, the Refractory Ward. I see that he appears to have settled a bit but is still rather agitated. Jim sits him in the chair and holds him down by the shoulders but as soon as I go near him with the razor he starts to struggle and twist his head from side to side. Jim grabs a hand towel and raps it tightly around the top of Psyche's head twisting it like a tourniquet to get a good grip. You wont see this method in any text book but it works a treat although it doesn't reduce the pain of shaving for Psyche. I decide enough is enough and I tell Jim I'm going to ask for more blades. You will be bloody lucky he replies.

As I enter the day room the charge nurse is propelling two more patients towards the bath room. He shouts "Get in there you scruffy sods" as he aims a kick narrowly missing one patient's backside. This time the patient is too alert and too agile to be caught off guard.

Suddenly I hear the sound of a key turning in the lock of the part glazed door from the dormitory and as Larry and I turn we see the diminutive dog collared figure of the Hospital Chaplain peering through the glass. He is Welsh and about sixty and his little screwed up face has more wrinkles than a prune. Suddenly everything changes to sweetness and light. Come in chaplain says Larry smiling benignly. I am captivated by this remarkable change in demeanour. Still intent on getting more razor blades I follow them both, past the row of cold, solitary, snotty nosed patients many with their jackets over their heads. The Chaplain doesn't speak or even look at them. He is too preoccupied with exchanging social pleasantries with the charge nurse. The patients are obviously of such little consequence that they are not even worth a brief weak acknowledgement or a fleeting smile. I follow them both a few steps behind as they enter the large day room and walk towards the bay window. They come to a halt and stand looking out of the window into the hospital grounds. The charge nurse is still in his alter ego, the epitome of good humour and gentlemanliness. The Chaplain catches sight of some daffodils in the grounds and says "look at all the beautiful flowers." Larry replies in dulcet tones "And they say there's no God." I cannot believe my ears. I don't know who is worse the Chaplain for his indifference to the patients or Larry for his blatant hypocrisy. Actually for differing reasons they are both equally hypocritical. They both move off towards the ward door . Larry opens it and ushers the Chaplain out with a cheery "Good Day" As the door closes I sense the time is right when he is still in the afterglow of sanctimonious self righteousness. Putting on my most pleasant expression I say "Can I have another few blades to finish the shaving? He doesn't reply but goes into the office and I hear his cupboard door open and shut. I'm almost sure I am onto a winner. He comes out without a word and holds out his hand with two blades in it. As I re-enter the bathroom Jim says "you took long enough, have you been making them? With a smile on my face, I hand him the two blades and he says "Jammy bugger, kiss his arse did you"?

The rest of the day passes uneventfully with just the usual endless chores of cleaning, preparing for meals and cleaning up afterwards. However it's been a good day, especially working with Jim who adds his own special dimension to alleviate some of the drudgery. The patients are lovely and the more deranged and peculiar they are the more I am drawn towards them. When I see what I have and what they have, which is virtually nothing, I understand more fully how lucky I am.

I've done three days on duty now and Jim went on his days off after yesterday's shift. I am left working with Shaun, who for the second time today has shown me how to prepare for bath day. He seems to think that rolling a vest and a pair of underpants up in a shirt with the patient's name tag uppermost requires a pass in at least 6 GCSE's. I'm sure that before the day is out he will take great pains to show me yet again. Yesterday he was telling Jim and me that his job during the war was flying back from Rome with wounded soldiers. According to Tinkerbelle during the flight they often had to amputate limbs without an anaesthetic and his job was to knock them out with a swift punch. He tells us this with a deadpan expression, while we can hardly keep a straight face. Jim and I just stand listening in feigned awe. We have discovered yet another fantasist disguised in a white coat. Behind his back Jim puts his forefinger to his head and rotates it mouthing the word "Screwball"

Psyche seems to have the wires on again as he has started hitting himself in the face. Shaun has been encouraging him saying "Give him another he deserves it." Two patients soiled themselves during the afternoon. It was very loose so by the time I got their trousers and shirt off the faeces had been distributed all the way down their legs onto their socks and up their backs into their hair, so I had no option but to give them a full bath and an entire change of clothes.

Tea time comes quickly and today it's hard boiled eggs. It's my turn to say grace which must be a ritual left over from the workhouse days when paupers were expected to be more than grateful for their meagre meals. As an agnostic I feel uncomfortable at uttering the words. It would be more appropriate if I just said "On your marks, Get Ready, Get set, Go" and fired a starting pistol. The ducks are all standing behind their chairs barely able to contain themselves and just itching to be first at the food. Before I can say the last words "May we be truly thankful" one of the patients, John Farrell, reaches out and grabs one of the eggs. In a split second it's in his mouth, shell and all and with a couple of gulps it's gone. Now the rest of the ducks are off. They are all seated, heads down, with their protective arms around their plates. Psyche has put half an egg into his mouth and is attempting to get two slices of bread and a cup of tea in simultaneously. His cheeks are distended like a hamster's. Suddenly he gags and a torrent of tea and soggy food explodes out of his mouth. Much of it hits the faces of those sitting opposite him but they don't even flinch. They just carry on cramming food into their mouths with pieces of egg and soggy bread sticking to their faces. Who would believe a scene like this? After this meal is over we again wipe them all down with wet towels. I think that after a week of this process we could boil their suits and make an excellent soup. In the evening we all settle down to watch TV until the arrival of the night staff.

Today is visiting day so after lunch every patient who is known to have visitors is dressed up in a new suit and clean shirt and tie and shoes. The tables are all set with nice cloths and the glass partition and door to the other day room are screened off with mobile bed screens. Then the nurses make a last minute adjustment to the privileged patients ties and buttons and smooth their hair down with a wet towel. When visiting time arrives those few patients receiving visitors are seated at the tables to await their loved ones, while all the others are herded behind the screens, out of sight in the other day room. This achieves two objectives. First most of the patients in their shabby stained suits are out of sight of the visitors and second these patients are unable to see all the goodies that will be given to the selected few. Even then some of them will try to attract the visitor's attention by tapping on the glass to beg for sweets or cigs, but it will be to no avail.

Now that most of the patients are secured in the second day room the main ward door is unlocked and left open. It will remain so for the 2 hours of visiting. I hear the first visitor clomping up the stone steps gasping for breath. It's Mrs Swinton; apparently she has been coming regularly for years, visiting John her schizophrenic son. She is a heavy woman who must be in her eighties. The charge nurse greets her as she enters and relieves her of her wicker basket. She stands for a moment and gasps "Those stairs will be the death of me;" Larry puts on his most charming smile and in a soft spoken voice says "Go on you are good for another twenty years yet." She beams in response, "How's my boy been, has he been a good boy?" Good boy! John is fifty if he's a day but he's still her boy and possibly always will be. Larry replies "He's fine , no trouble at all" but he doesn't mention the clip he gave him along the ear this morning. She breathlessly clutches her chest and takes a seat at the table opposite John. I note how shabby her clothes are and how her hair looks unwashed, lank and unkempt. From where I am sitting I can see the backs of her legs which are criss-crossed with tortuous blue black varicose veins. Her ankles look very swollen and they overlap the sides of her shabby down at the heel brown shoes. She does not look in good health but she is his Mum and she apparently comes several miles to be here, winter or summer, rain or shine. That's real devotion for you.

More visitors have arrived and Larry glides from table to table like the sugar plum fairy, stopping noticeably longer where there are attractive women visitors. Occasionally he will pat a patient affectionately on the head and utter a caring word or two. He is all sweetness and light and it appears he loves all the patients like a father. Quite touching really if you didn't know the truth. The next two hours seem like ten as I sit like a sentry by the ward door. To relieve the monotony I have drifted in and out of day dreams and have glanced at the ceiling, floor and visitors a thousand times as the hour hand of the ward clock moves imperceptibly on its journey towards 4 o'clock.

At last visiting has drawn to an end. Several visitors have already left saying goodbye as they pass me. Having stuffed the patients up to the eyeballs most have also left cakes, money, sweets and cigarettes to be locked in the charge nurse's office cupboard. I doubt if they will ever be seen again. The last relatives finally filter out and the patients are corralled back into the other day room to have their best suits quickly taken off and replaced with their usual shabby stained clothes. For a few hours they have looked like human beings and have been the centre of attention and now each will return to just being a long stay chronic patients, just one lost soul amongst many.

Last week my wife and I visited Peter, a blind member of her family who is a patient in Prudhoe Monkton Mental Handicap Hospital. When we entered the large villa where he was held the place looked barren and almost deserted. We were greeted by the charge nurse who ushered us to a bay window where Peter was sitting alone at a bare wooden table. The place was freezing and after an hour talking to Peter and feeding him goodies I developed an urgent need to go to the loo. Having explained my need to the charge nurse he directed me toward the backs. As I opened the door I was confronted by an ante-room that could best be described as looking and feeling like a butcher's cold storage room. Sitting around the room on wooden benches were about twenty silent white and blue faced patients dressed in the usual shabby garb. In an attempt to keep warm some were vigorously rubbing their hands and faces, others had their jackets pulled over their heads breathing inside their jacket to try to generate some heat. Others had their cold hands thrust deep into their coat pockets. All of them looked dejected and thoroughly miserable. How long they had been in the room or how long they would remain I can only guess. It was likely to be at least two hours. It struck me that this was the same uncaring system that existed in my hospital but here the conditions appeared to be even worse and this is in a hospital with an international reputation. It is the hospital that discovered the first nappy test for detecting

Phenylketonuria a condition that causes progressive brain deterioration in newborn babies if undetected and untreated. We left forlorn blind little Peter sitting alone at the window. I haven't seen him since and doubt if I will ever see him again.

I have been on Ward 16 for three weeks now. Yesterday evening we had to clear the day room to make way for the decorators who are going to give it a spruce up. This morning they have erected scaffolding to reach the highest part of the walls and ceiling. It's Jim's day off so I am expecting a routine bound day with a repeat lecture on some other basic practice like shirt and underwear wrapping. I sense Tinkerbelle is in a bad mood as he has been allocating me jobs in a very terse and abrupt way. For several weeks now I have studied him carefully and to be honest I don't like the man's personality or his attitude towards patients. He's of short but stocky build and he always has his white coat sleeves rolled up displaying his powerful forearms. His hair is black and combed straight back. His eyes are deep set and have a strange intent glint. With his scowling face and Irish accent he reminds me of a malevolent leprechaun. He has either a speech impediment or it is part of his Irish pronunciation but words such as Think he pronounces as TINK. He will say for example "I tink we should do this" or "I tink we should do that". Jimmy had caught onto this

very quickly and had given him the nickname of
TINK-ABELLE.

The painters have now gone to the canteen and the
patients have finished dinner. I'm at a loose end
when Shaun approaches me and thrusts a comb and
a pair of scissors into my hand and tells me curtly to
do a few haircuts. Psyche has been very agitated all
morning and has been constantly disturbing the
painters by wandering in and out of their scaffolding
towers. Shaun, who has been watching him with
barely suppressed anger, has kept moving him into
the other day room. The presence of the painters
appears to have kept the lid on the situation.

Suddenly I hear Psyche shout out from close behind
me. Tinkerbelle swings round towards him his face
distorted in anger, "Come here you bastard" He
moves quickly towards Psyche and grabs his hair in
a powerful grip dragging him towards the
scaffolding. Twice he savagely smacks the side of
Psyche's head against the horizontal steel bar, while
Psyche cries out and tries to break free. Tinkerbelle
responds with even greater force, cursing "bastard-
bastard-bastard" as his powerful arms pound
Psyche's head against the unyielding metal.
Suddenly he releases his grip on Psyche's hair and
Psyche reels away without a word. It's another
savage message that you don't mess with anyone in
a white coat.

Tinkerbelle turns towards me with a face as black as thunder then storms off out of the day room. I continue with my hair cutting task and the painters return from lunch while Psyche does his modified goose step up and down the ward, at intervals shouting out and again hitting himself in the face. It's all just part of the reality of living and working here. The thought has crossed my mind that I am one member of staff working on one shift on one ward. There are 12 wards and four shifts a week. What is the total number of acts of savagery, cruelty and neglect perpetrated here by staff? Nobody knows but it is certainly much greater than I have witnessed. Even the doctors appear to show little regard for or interest in chronic long stay patients. On this ward doctors give a bare minimum of their time. When I do see them come into the ward they go straight into the charge nurse's office then straight out again and away. The rare occasion they do see a patient is when one is very ill either mentally or physically or when they carry out the 6 monthly mandatory physical examination. The managers routinely stroll through the ward on their "rounds" and pass the time of day in conversation with the charge nurse, then they too are gone. The charge nurses hold the real power here; they are the ones really in control. It entirely depends on them how the patients are treated. They control the patient's comfort money, the accident report books and stock control books. It is said that some keep two sets of records, one for themselves and one for admin office. More importantly they assess the staff's performance so it is very unwise to get on their "wrong side". They are also the backbone of a Union that holds more real power than the managers. None of them have been promoted on merit or have come from other hospitals. Promotion is by filling "dead men's shoes." All promotion is from within the hospital, you just bide your time and you are promoted first to deputy charge nurse then charge nurse. The managers are also promoted from within the hospital but I am not sure what the process is. The one thing the managers and charge nurses have in common is that they have all come through an even more cruel and neglectful era. I have been told by a number of old charge nurses that prior to 1948, when the National Health Service came into being that the conditions were even worse for patients than they are now. An additional factor is that some managers and charge nurses share personal and family friendships outside work. Put all of these aspects together and it would be difficult to find a more fertile ground for collusion than this place.

Five weeks have now passed and the painters have finished their work. Larry the charge nurse is on compassionate leave. We have just heard that his daughter, who I think was his only child, has committed suicide by jumping off the top of a high rise block of flats in the east of the city. Nobody seems to know why she was in that locality or why apparently she chose to kill herself there. Under these tragic circumstances I think it may be a long time before Larry returns to work.

Today I am scheduled for another boring day working without Jim and with Shaun in charge. I know its going to be boring because it's visiting day and this time I have been allocated for two hours to look after those patients without visitors. This means I will be the only member of staff locked in the second day room. The room itself is barely heated, the furniture is Spartan, there are no pictures, flowers, ornaments or rugs, just bare wood floors. There are no diversions in this room such as TV, books or games and few if any of the patients can string more than two coherent sentences together, but despite this I love them all and. I am not alone in this respect, Several of the trained staff I have worked with on this ward, battle hardened and routine bound as they are, have shown nothing but patience and kindness towards the patients. We know that most of these poor buggers only have night and day to mark the passage of time. They have none of those little events and milestones that make life meaningful and enjoyable, like christenings, birthdays, weddings. They have no relatives or friends to care for them or visit them , all that is pleasurable for them is very basic, like eating, drinking and solitary masturbation or DIY sex as

Jim calls it. To add to their misery there are those in white coats that control their every movement. In some their black depression is unremitting and in others inner voices torment them night and day. In the long run only death will relieve them of all their afflictions.

Two o'clock has come and gone and I am locked in the long day room with the patients who have no visitors.. An hour has passed and I'm going slowly mad with boredom. The patients are all sitting alongside the wall many with their jackets over their heads either for comfort or to shut out reality for a short while. The pale spring sunshine streams in through the windows, its beams lighting up a myriad of tiny dancing dust particles. Its a beautiful and hypnotic sight and I watch fascinated for a few minutes. Then I'm back in tune with the deafening silence that is occasionally broken by a patient shuffling into the backs to relieve himself, often returning to his seat with his flies open or his shirt hanging over his trousers. I walk towards the bay window and look out with a fixed stare, my brain frozen by inactivity, boredom and having to listen to endless gibberish. Across the grounds towards the high perimeter wall, the people in the houses just over the main road have faced the perimeter wall for almost a hundred years and they haven't an inkling, apart from rumour about what goes on over this side. This is a strange isolated world within the real world, it's a world that has its own hierarchy, its own serfs, its own culture with rigid rules and an unchallengeable code of secrecy. Even sane people like myself could go mad in here if they were confined for any length of time. Certainly many nurses who work here are almost as institutionalised as the patients. I know this place inside out now, its buildings, its paths, its fields and gardens, many of its staff and a good number of its patients. The first part of the hospital was established in 1866 and was more fully opened in 1869. It stood in 60 acres of land and was built of austere grey black stone blocks. Its of a linear design with all the wards running south off one main corridor that is about ¼ of a mile long. The eastern end of the building is the male side and the west is for the females. In the centre separating the two sides is a locked library. It's a sort of No Man's Land or if you prefer No Woman's Land. To pass through from one side to the other requires a male key to enter from our side and a female key to enter the women's side. Total segregation is achieved by the fact that male staff are not issued with a female key and vice versa. The two sides of the hospital are run entirely separately, one has a Matron and we have Mr Gibbons our Chief Male Nurse. Even the shift patterns are different. Contact between male and female patients is restricted to events held in the main hall. As I look forlornly out of the window again I catch sight of work under way to dismantle the airing court walls.

Now that is progress, getting rid of these prison like edifices. Turning away from the window to look for some other means of relieving the boredom my attention rests on a patient with catatonic schizophrenia. He has been standing in a corner on one leg with one arm raised above his head for quite a long time now, which is a feat well outside the ability of a normal person. Even when we put him in bed at night he hold his hand up above his head. As I approach him he doesn't move and looks straight ahead. When I say his name he doesn't respond and his wax like features don't portray any sign of recognition. He has been like this for weeks. I notice his hand has turned a bluish colour and when I touch it, it is very cold through lack of blood being able to reach the hand being held two feet above his head for such a long time. It's puzzling why some forms of schizophrenia manifest themselves in this way. It's also rather a mystery how he is able to balance and bear the discomfort. I take hold of his hand to place it by his side and I can feel him resisting but finally manage to get it down. With some effort I walk him to a chair and sit him down. I sense that he doesn't like what I am doing but this is more about my intuition than actually knowing. In this type of work sometimes all you have to go on is intuition which is refined over time by observation and experience. A few minutes later when I look at him again he is standing on one leg with a hand raised above his head.

I can hear sounds of movement in the next day room and realise that visiting time is almost over. Thank God! I hear the key in the lock and Tinkerbelle comes through and gives me one of his rare smiles. He certainly doesn't have a lot of patience so no doubt he's pleased that he no longer has to do the rounds of visitors dishing out homespun caring platitudes. The rest of the day passes quickly with the usual routine of serving tea, clearing away, dishing out the evening beverages and watching TV until the night nurse comes on.

Larry Docherty is back on duty today. Since his return it has been obvious that the death of his daughter has greatly affected him. Jim and I have determined to keep in the background and not to trouble him in any way. For most of the time this morning he has stayed in the office only emerging to dole out some cigarettes to the patients. There's no attempt to cause a rugby scrum this time.

Dinner is finished now and the clearing away has been done. Tinkerbelle has told me to go on second lunch with Jim. As we set off down the corridor I spot my friend Bill the Communist ahead of us and I see a flash of bright red coming from the bottom of his boots. His one fixed knee joint makes him a slow walker and we quickly catch him up. He turns round as I tap him on the shoulder, "What's with the boots

Bill." He laughs and lifts up his foot to show me the soles. They are bright red and about half an inch thick. "Off cuts of lino Mac they will never wear out" He tells me that when the workmen finished laying the corridor lino that they left piles of off cuts. He took a few pieces and cut them to shape and soled his boots with them. Thats ingenuity for you but he could have chosen a better and less obvious colour.

Arriving at the staff Café we get our meal and are joined by a rather aloof junior student nurse who has a distinctly superior air. We don't know his name but we have seen him around, characteristically with a medical book stuck under his arm. We know he lives in the nurse's home within the grounds of the hospital. As we eat our dinner he engages us in conversation asking us if we know nurse Ann Smith. What a question, do we know Ann Smith. Every hot blooded male nurse in the hospital fancies her, she is beautiful. We both casually reply, "Yes we know her!" I wonder what's coming next. He follows on "I had a terrible experience last night." Jim and I anticipate there's going to be something interesting here. What was that we ask. Well he replies "I was fast asleep in bed when I was woken up by someone climbing into my bed." Jim and I look at each other; this is getting even more interesting. Who was that we enquire? It was Ann Smith he replies with a slightly distasteful look on his face. I think to myself

Ann Smith, my God it's almost unthinkable, he must be going to engage us in a serious case of bragging. Not quite believing what I am hearing I ask what happened then? Well he replies I said to her that she was disgusting and told her to leave my room immediately. Jim and I look at each other across the table amazed and wide eyed. This has a ring of truth about it; I had expected bragging but he's actually complaining. Not one student in a hundred would say they kicked her out of bed. My view of him is now fully confirmed, he is a total twit. Even telling us this story shows that he has absolutely no insight into how this story will be perceived. What on earth was Ann Smith thinking about? The only conclusion can be that she was either sleep walking, desperate or blind drunk or in this case all three. As we walk back to the ward Jim and I are incredulous and we laugh and joke about it all the way back to the ward door.

Thinking about the nurses home in general this is another one of those enigmas associated with this hospital. The home is a large building situated in the grounds just opposite the church. The rooms for the male students are on the ground floor and those for females are on the first floor. There are two staircases situated at either end of the building that allow every resident, male or female, free and unfettered access to both floors. At 11pm the female night matron visits the home to ensure that everyone is in. If they are not then they are in for a ticking off on their return, the implication being that if you are out after 11 pm you have been up to no good. However after she has left male and female nurses can mix unhindered to do exactly as they wish. The Church is another hot spot for sexual liaisons. Its attractions are threefold, first both the male and female door keys fit the locks, second it is heated during inclement weather and third sex and sacrilege seem to produce an additional vicarious thrill. They say it's very exiting to be indulging in inter-sex liaisons on a moonlight night with the moonbeams streaming in highlighting up the figures of the saints in the stained glass windows. Nothing is sacred here.

As we enter through the ward door Larry comes out of his office, beckons me in and sits me down at the side of his desk. I'm a bit unsure what this is all about and think maybe I have done something wrong. He takes his seat and rather uncharacteristically for such a rugged and blunt man he tells me of his daughters death and the possibility of life after death. He says he has been studying spiritualism and that has been given the address of a local medium who he hopes will put him in contact with his daughter. I don't know why he has chosen to speak to me about such a deep and personal matter, maybe he is speaking to lots of people to offload his sorrow and to obtain some solace. He then passes me a number of spiritualist magazines and says "have look at these and tell me what you think." For the next five minutes I scan through them, particularly the pictures that show clouds of ectoplasm coming from medium's mouths and bodies. To say that I am sceptical of these pictures and the claims of contact with the dead is an understatement, honestly I think they are a load of trickery to entrap susceptible people in their grief. So when I have finished looking at the magazines and he asks me again "what do you think," realising that he is deeply troubled and desperately hoping to contact his dead daughter or find out why she apparently committed suicide, I just utter a few noncommittal words in response "very interesting, makes you think doesn't it." This seems to satisfy him so I quietly leave the office.

Two days later when I am back on duty he calls me into the office again. As usual he sitting at his desk. He beckons me towards a chair and says "take a seat." I'm not sure what it is that singles me out for these sessions, maybe it's just because I absorb his out pouring like a sponge. He leans forward, looks at me intently, and says "I went to see a medium at her home last night and she was remarkable. She had never met or heard of me yet as soon as she opened the door she took hold of my hands and said to me "you have healing hands." This first encounter has obviously totally convinced him but for me, having now heard her utterances, it totally convinces me that she is a charlatan. Healing hands, never, yet I find myself silently moving my head up and down to indicate agreement. Nevertheless I do feel very sorry for him, to lose an only daughter under these awful circumstances must be a terrible blow and not without the engendering of some sense of personal guilt.

He rises from his chair and picks up a pile of spiritualist magazines and ushers me towards the door. He then leads me up the ward towards the locker room. Opening the door he places the pile of magazines on the wooden table in front of me and tells me to take a chair. "Have a look at these and tell me what you think." Without a further word he leaves the room and locks the door behind him. The room has a window that overlooks the exhilarating sight of the main corridor roof. It has a row of steel lockers, a scrubbed robust wood table and a chair and its bleak and bloody cold. Worse still I cannot get out as here as there is no key hole on the inside, I am trapped. For a few moments I just sit and think to myself, what the hell's going on here. As I stare vacantly at the magazines I start to flick through them; there are about a doæn. Even if I was interested, and I am not, I wouldn't read this amount in one go, but knowing he's going to question me about them I start reluctantly to read. After about an hour I'm finding it hard to concentrate, I'm very cold, bored and annoyed that he's locked me in here.

I have tried knocking on the door but nobody appears to have heard me. Another hour passes and I have finished all the reading I can manage. I have stood at the window but there's nothing to see other than the tiled top of a roof. It's now near to dinner time and I can hear footsteps, then the sound of the key turning in the door lock, thank god. The door swings open and I see the smiling face of Docherty, I could kill him "read them all then" he queries? "We will discuss them after dinner, go now and give the staff a hand."

When dinner is finished I am recalled to Larry's office to be cross examined about my reaction to the spiritualist books I was presented with. In response to his probing questions it is difficult to give him an answer that won't offend his beliefs and one that will not convey that he will be able to contact his dead daughter. Somehow my responses appear to satisfy him. He brings the session to a close and I hastily leave his office. Outside I ponder about him. He is a rough and ready type but he isn't a bad old stick really and he is obviously deeply psychologically troubled. His approach to the patients reflects his general roughness and lack of insight. I have witnessed the occasional heavy slap across the back of the head and neck and the kicks in the pants accompanied by bad language but I have never seen him dish out the severe type of punishment I have seen on other wards. His theft of the patient's and ward goods is also nothing unusual. It's just part of the general scene here. With me he appears to have taken a strict but kindly fatherly approach. I ponder how easy it is to quickly come to accept this rough and uncaring type of behaviour as normal.

Two days later, during my so called days off doing my part time job, the circumstances surrounding Larry become even more ludicrous. I am in the process of making mock wooden Victorian wall lights and Alan my boss is in the corner of the workshop making what looks like a large brass trumpet. What on earth is that I ask? He replies "they are trumpets to magnify sound. I am making four for Larry Docherty to hang up in the corner of his room." He sees my perplexed look and continues "they are to hear the spirit voices." I reply "go on who are you kidding." Alan smiles, "honest no joking they are for Larry to hear the spirit voices." Now I have heard it all, a charge nurse in a mental hospital doing spirit writing and hoping to hear voices from the dead from four brass trumpets hanging up in the corners of his sitting room. If someone other than Alan had told me this I wouldn't have believed him. To be blunt it appears to me that Docherty is completely unhinged, too unhinged to be teaching student nurses.

Three days later, back on the ward at 7 am I am greeted by a rather dejected Jim, who informs me that he has just been notified that he has failed for the second time his final exams to become a State Registered Mental Nurse. Worse still he has also been told that there is no point in his seeking a third attempt. It's a severe blow to his self esteem but everything has not been lost, as on the strength of the three year training he has completed he can apply to become a State Enrolled Nurse which is a lesser qualification but one that still allows him to be employed as a trained nurse. When I think of some of the trained nurses I have met whose behaviour is a disgrace to the profession I feel that there is no justice in the world, and of course there isn't.

Larry's off today and Tinkerbelle is in charge. After morning tea he has decided to have some fun with little Charlie Bates. He has got a very large white coat from the store and put it on Charlie. The sleeves hang well over his hands and the bottom of the coat almost touches the floor. Charlie with his little coconut head sprouting hair in all directions looks like a dressed up little grinning chimpanzee; but he's loving it and unfortunately we cannot stop laughing. Tinkerbelle adds a few adornments, a stethoscope around his neck and a name badge and then leads him into Larry's office. With mock courtesy he sits Charlie down on Larry's chair and puts a pad of paper on the desk in front of him. Next he places a pen in his hand and says to Charlie "Doctor can you write a prescription for one of the patients." Charlie is in his element having all this attention and he grins from ear to ear talking his usual gibberish incessantly. Charlie takes the pen a scribbles away. Then he is asked to answer the phone. This is a little more difficult for him and he gets the handset upside down and does not quite know what to do with it. This produces another spate of laughter from the staff. His appearance and performance on one level are an absolute scream but I am aware that on another level, it's so sad. After a while the fun begins to wear a little thin and Tinkerbelle ends it by standing Charlie up and removing the white coat and stethoscope. Someone rewards Charlie by giving him a cigarette for his performance and he shuffles out of the office apparently, briefly, a happy little man.

Out in the day room I spot one of my favourite patients walking towards me, he is called John Farrell. We are not supposed to have favourites but being human we all do and I am no exception. John is a small, shy, emaciated elfin like creature. He is so thin that the shoulder pads of his dishevelled jacket hang down half way to his elbows. He never speaks but on occasion will mutter in response to a question. If you really strain your ears you may just catch him making a response of yes or no. His strangest feature is his face. It's quite unlike any other I have seen.

It's as white as a sheet. The few remaining strands of his hair are swept across his dome like head and his ears stick out prominently like open doors. The muscles of both his eyelids don't function, so both his eyes remain shut. To counter this to be able to see, he holds his head back and keeps one eyelid up with the forefinger of his left hand. Over the years the consequence of this has been to produce deep upward furrows on his forehead above his left eye. His existence on the ward follows the usual pattern of almost total isolation, from everyone both patients and staff alike. Most of the wards in this hospital have 30, 40 or even 60 patients and it is rare for any friendships to develop; it is even unusual to hear patients meaningfully talking to each other. John stops in front of me as if he wants to say something but no words come out. He stands immediately in front of me as if he is studying an interesting freak of nature. Then after a moment he turns and walks unsteadily away. I cannot even hazard a guess what the purpose of his scrutiny was or what thoughts were passing through his mind. Due to the frequent movement of students to gain a wide range of experience it is unlikely that I will ever see him again or any of the other patients I have become attached to.

Today is hospital open day when the public can have a guided tour of the hospital. I have been allocated two jobs. In the morning I am to act as a guide and in the afternoon I am serving tea in the patient's cafeteria. Trekking around the wards this morning has been quite interesting with lots of questions from the groups I have escorted. It's now afternoon and the café is quite full. I have discarded my white coat in favour of my new grey hospital suit. I have filled two very large metal tea pots full to the brim. Trying to be clever I have taken one in each hand and they weigh a ton. As I approach the first table to serve four women sitting there the thin metal handles on the tea pots are cutting into my fingers. As the ladies push their cups towards the kettles seem to be getting heavier, the pain is excruciating and my hands begin to shake with the strain. The consequence is that as I begin to pour the tea it not only goes into the cups but splashes all over the saucers and table. I finally manage to fill the cups and move quickly to put one of the pots down on the counter. As I move away I hear one of the women say to the other "Poor young chap, did you see how his hands were shaking. I wonder what he is in here for?" This is the second time I have been mistaken for a patient. The first time was at a patient's dance in the hospital hall. This time it came from an old long stay toothless female patient I was having a dance with. She asked me when was I admitted and what ward was I on.

Back on the ward for the rest of the day I am relieved that I only have two working days left on the ward. My next placement is in Oedema Hall.

When I have completed my time there I will be sitting my final examination and if I pass I will have reached the dizzy heights of becoming a fully trained nurse. I will also get £50 if I pass which I desperately need, now that I have two young children and another on the way. Having only my wages to support us I have had to continue working at three jobs.

CHAPTER 6

OEDEMA HALL

Getting out of bed in the dark on a Sunday at 5.30 a.m. is no joke and I have little enthusiasm at the prospect of working 12 hour shifts on yet another geriatric ward, especially Oedema Hall.

When I arrive at the hospital at 7.15 the main corridor is eerily quiet and deserted. The lead off corridor down to the ward is in semi darkness and as I approach the wards stout green wooden door I think of Jim's remark "Abandon hope all ye who enter here." Unlocking the door I step into a vast unlit day room. The first thing I notice is the musty stale smell of urine soaked clothing. A pale yellow light shines through a doorway ahead of me and I can hear the noise of movement and the rattling of cot sides coming from inside. As my eyes become more accustomed to the gloom I can see more clearly rows of dark brown tables and chairs. Suddenly there is a loud rasping fart followed by another just as loud coming from the corner of the room where an old man is sitting with his head lolling on a table in front of him. I suppose those two fart; are an appropriate greeting. As I walk slowly towards the lit door I see another old man sitting silently in a wheelchair in the centre of the room. I stop to look at him more intently. It is immediately apparent that he only has one leg as his trouser is wrapped up and pushed underneath his stump while his other foot is in a crumpled slipper. His trousers are undone and open around his belly and his shirt is gaping open exposing a large area of white blotchy stomach. On his table are a metal urine bottle, a sputum mug, a pipe a tobacco tin and a half eaten wizened orange. He starts to wheeze and gives a throaty cough as he stares vacantly into the gloom seemingly unaware of my presence. As I pass through the door into the brightly lit dormitory I am greeted by the deputy charge nurse. My first reaction is that he looks a bit of a spiv. After a brief introduction he says "go and give the lads a help with the beds." As I cast my eyes around the room to see who I can help I see that there are four long rows of occupied beds, there must be at least fifty. Down the centre of the room is a row of pillars and at the far end wall I can see a number of doors to side rooms. From one of these rooms a nurse emerges and walks towards me. As he gets near he smiles and holds out his hand and in broken English says "I John Pali, staff nurse you come give me a hand." Walking down the right side of the ward where the more able patients appear to be, we start getting some of them up. The first two or three beds are soaking and stained with excreta. The patient's themselves are wet up to the neck; to get in this state they must have been lying in a soaked bed for hours. The night staff are supposed to do a wet round every two hours during the night but I doubt if they bothered with these patients last night. There's a saying in the hospital that a tidy counterpane can hide a multitude of sins and that is certainly true in this case. Much depends on who is on night duty and how caring they are. As we move up the row of beds I see a number of spherical balls of hard shit on the floor in front of me and as I look two more land on the floor in front of me in quick succession. Looking towards the direction they came from I see a patient in the process of carefully rolling another ball in his hands. As he finishes his creation he deftly flicks it into the aisle. What his intention is or what he is thinking of is beyond me. John notices what's going on and asks me to have a look at the patient and to make sure I wash his hands. As I attend to him I see that he also has some faeces sticking to his hair. When I inform John of this he tells me to leave his hair until bath time. He then informs me that all the patients in the beds with cot sided beds on the other side of the ward will to be put in the bath, starting with the dirtiest first.

It appears that I have drawn the short straw again as the deputy charge nurse informs me that a staff nurse and I have been allocated to the bathroom. The rest of the staff will wheel the patients in on commode chairs and then remake the beds ready for the patients to return. The bathroom is just like all the others I have worked in. Cold white tiles, stone floors and Victorian high sided cast iron baths. The staff nurse I am working with has a rather chiselled, high cheek boned Mediterranean look with dark tight wavy hair and rather horsy features. His manner can be best described as alternating between brusqueness and indifference. He informs me that I need to strip down to my vest as he hands me a large thick red rubber knee length apron. As I fill the bath for the first time I use the wooden bath thermometer to check that the water is not too hot to scald. I can sense his impatience with this procedure and it is quite obvious that he feels this is a waste of time.

When the first patient is wheeled in we grab him under the arms and knees and unceremoniously swing him into the bath. As soon as his bum hits the water he tries to steady himself by desperately clutching at the bath sides. What follows next is what my grandmother would call a cat's lick or a sheep dip. There is certainly nothing genteel about the way the staff nurse does the bathing and he ends the session by pouring a large jug of cold water over the head of the patient without warning. The patient gets quite a shock and shouts out bugger, bugger, bugger as we lift him out of the bath. Again he grips the sides of the bath and will not let go. For this the staff nurse gives him a sharp rap across both knuckles with a long handled wooden bath brush. The next three patients follow in quick succession and receive the same cursory attention. At the point when we are about to receive the fourth patient someone shouts through the door that breakfast is up. Divesting ourselves of our protective rubber aprons we return to the dormitory where the meal trolley is standing. As I look at what's on offer the word revolting springs to mind. There is a large, deep aluminium tin full to the brim with soggy bread floating in hot milk. On the top of the milk is what looks like an oil slick which I am informed is margarine. A nurse tells me that this slop is called Boily and it's made for those patients without teeth. Next to the Boily tin is another large but shallow tin full of minced bacon floating in fat. It looks like grapeshot and there are more white granules in it than red. It looks more like minced fat than minced bacon.

The task I have been given is to feed the most deteriorated and ill patients with this stomach churning stuff. It's not as easy as I thought as my first two patients are reluctant to open their mouths. Seeing this the deputy charge nurse comes across looking rather exasperated. He takes the spoon out of my hand, then pinches the patient nose until he runs short of breath and opens his mouth. Then in goes a full spoonful of slop. He then holds the patients jaw closed until he swallows. As he turns to go he says "There you are, that's how you do it, if you don't you will be there all bloody day." Despite the fact that what he has shown me works I am determined to continue with a more persuasive approach. I have more success with the minced bacon; the patients appear to like the taste more but occasionally they spit it out with apparent disgust and my white coat gets peppered with it. Predictably I am last to finish the feeding and I am curtly dismissed from the dormitory back into the bathroom. Back in our red rubber aprons we start again on a seemingly endless conveyer belt of patients. They are all resistive and clutch anything they come into contact with, which includes the bath sides, our clothing and our hands and arms. They have the strength of desperation and it is often very difficult to release their grip. On occasion their nails dig deep into the exposed skin of our arms and hands even to the extent that they draw blood. They also try to bite our arms and hands. Some patients have huge sacral bed sores exposing the bone. Fred the staff nurse is becoming more and more impatient and rough. He looks at me with an exasperated look and says " We are behind schedule so don't empty the bath this time." So the next three patients go into the same bath water which has now turned brown. We then break for lunch and an hour later when we return it's straight back into the bathroom. There's a number of frail ill patients to finish and Fred has devised a a more effective method to speed their exit from the bath. He now pours several jugs of cold water over their heads. Actually this doesn't work; it makes matters worse but he obviously gets a kick out of hearing the old men shout out. Finally by mid afternoon we get to the more able patients and again it's three or four patients put in the same bathwater. The combination of condensation in the bathroom and the splashes from patients flailing about has completely soaked me. My shoes are sodden and have lost all their colour and my back aches from lifting patients in and out of the bath and bending over the bath to clean their hindquarters. The skin on my hands and fingers is shrivelled up and they feel awful. This Marathon process of bathing is truly not the most wonderful aspect of mental nursing. The last man to receive a bath is Old Tom the ward worker. He is a lovely old man with silver white hair who works silently from morning to night washing and cleaning, emptying urine bottles and sputum mugs. He is holding the taps to steady himself and has got one leg over into the bath but cannot manage to get the other over. Fred reaches for a mop standing in the corner and with some force pushes the handle up Toms backside. Tom gives a shout of pain and just manages to get his other foot into the bath. Fred looks pleased with himself "That made you move you old bugger, didn't it." When Fred leaves the bathroom I check Tom's rear end and luckily there doesn't appear to be any damage but that assault could have resulted in severe injuries to his rectum. As we finish I think to myself, why is it that all the patients have to be sheep dipped on a Sunday. It's beyond me, it would be much less arduous if we did a few baths each day and then we could also do a much better job. The rest of the day until 7 pm is spent in the usual way changing beds and feeding patients. Leaving the ward at night I reflect on what I have seen and wonder what tomorrow will bring.

Today I am pleased to see that John Pali and another staff nurse are on duty. It's now mid morning and the deputy charge nurse hasn't moved his backside yet, he is a lazy devil. Touchy one of the more able patients is making his way towards me through the dayroom. He's another strange little fellow. His dishevelled dress is the same as that of all the other patients except for two features. One he always has his trousers tucked into his socks and two he always wears his cap, even when in bed. The reason he has been nicknamed Touchy is that if you tap him on the head he goes berserk. A number of nurses delight in seeing his reaction when they reach for his head. Consequently he has become very adept at weaving and ducking. This ability to avoid being touched seems to add spice to the game. As Touchy walks through the doorway into the dormitory the deputy charge nurse leaps out from behind the door and grabs Touchy's cap. He then throws it up in the air and kicks it as it falls towards the ground. The force of the kick dislodges the lining of the cap and it flutters out along with a large number of pound notes. On seeing this amount of hidden money the look on the deputy charge nurse's face is a picture; all that money and he never guessed it was there. Just then I hear a gruff voice behind me "What have we here then, best count it and put it into the admin office." It's the Assistant Chief Male Nurse Tommy Marks or as we call him Groucho. His walk is identical to that of Groucho Marks. The deputy charge nurse can hardly hide his crestfallen look. All that money could have been his but there is no way he can avoid counting it and handing it in to the office. What a hoot, I cannot avoid laughing to myself. It's great to see this potential thief foiled.

During a rare lull in the work I take the opportunity to walk down between the rows of beds. The patients with the cot sides look terribly frail. Some are on their backs, their skin deathly pale and wax like with spidery blue veins just below the skin. Some look with sightless pale watery eyes towards the ceiling their mouths wide open displaying toothless gums. They have blue tinged lips and sunken cheeks. I stop to talk to one who is sitting up and rattling his cot sides. I see by the coal scratches on his forehead and nose that in the distant past he has been a miner. Although his mind has gone I know from previous experience that his thin muscular body is still as strong as a pit prop and he has a grip of iron from years of working with a pick and shovel. "What have you been doing today" I ask him. He replies in a strong Durham accent "well hinny aa bin doon the pit, done a full shift, then went yem to me missus." I know of course that this is complete fantasy. He has been in his bed for weeks and his wife died five years ago. It's pitiful really. After such a hard life he shouldn't have to die here. I have been told that living in this type of fantasy world is called confabulation. It occurs when people with dementia fill in their memory gaps with what they used to do in the past. Maybe it's a good thing that they are removed from reality.

John breaks my train of thought by shouting to me. He is gesturing toward the double glass doors at the side of the dormitory. I dutifully follow him into what appears to be a large lean-to greenhouse. Unbelievably I have entirely missed the fact that this is another patient area. It's bloody freezing, The entire side and the roof are glass and I can feel a strong cold draft coming from the ill fitting steel framed windows. The floor is stone and all the lockers are metal. The place looks barren with no decoration or radio or TV. It's like a large dilapidated greenhouse. A row of emaciated blue tinged white faced patients sit in cold starched white linen sheets, motionless facing the windows. It appears like a mortuary for the living. John calls me across and tells me this is the TB veranda. In response I tell him that I didn't even know it was here. He rebukes me by saying " You asleep half the time, you bloody useless." Although I am taken aback by this response I cannot deny what he has said as it's the truth, what with doing three jobs and going to bed late I am like a zombie until about midday. John points to a sputum mug that has spilt its yellow, white and green gooey mess across the floor. As he leaves the veranda he tells me curtly "You get bucket and mop and clean up." It must have been a patient or old Tom who has knocked the pot over. As I look closer I see that the contents have slithered down the side of the bed cover. Returning with a bucket full of disinfectant and a mop I set about the task of cleaning it up. As soon as I apply the mop the goo seems to slide even further across the floor. Its just another one of those revolting jobs we have to do here. As I leave the veranda I notice that the man near to the door appears to be close to death.

A week has now passed and my intuition regarding the deputy charge nurse is stronger than ever. Like a few other senior staff I have worked with he does very little, spending most of his time in the glass fronted office, talking on the phone or reading the papers. He never helps with the bed changing or dressings and disappears off the ward several times a day. He has just beckoned me to follow him across the day room, for what reason I cannot guess. He then ushers me into the kitchen and stops in the centre of the floor and with a gesture like Sir Walter Raleigh laying down his cape for the Queen he sweeps his lowered hand towards the fridge. His face registers a look of total amazement as he snatches at the fridge door handle and jerks it open. He then pointedly stares at an empty shelf and with a note of complete surprise says to me "Look the eggs have gone, someone must have stolen two trays of eggs." I think to myself, yep and I know who has stolen them and I have just been set up as a witness. As we return to the dormitory office he announces in a loud voice "someone has stolen the eggs out of the fridge" and turning to me he says "isn't that so." I nod in agreement and think to myself, what an amateur, who does he think he is kidding? By the staff's expression I think they have also rumbled his little game.

Just before lunch John asks me to accompany him on a bed-round to dress the bed sores of some of the most ill patients. Having first set up a sterile dressing trolley we roll the first patient on his side and he cries out in pain and clutches my white coat. As I remove the large dressing on his backside I see a large area of black necrotic flesh surrounded by a red, deep suppurating cavity. Watching John applying a de-sloughing cream to the dead tissue and the barrier cream to the surrounding skin I notice how gentle and painstaking he is. To the patient he says "you feel better soon." After the final sterile pad is applied he pushes a pillow onto the patient's back and tells him that this is to support him and keep him on his side for a couple of hours. This is typical of John. Everything he does is done with care and compassion, he is without doubt a fantastic nurse. I often wonder if he thinks that some of us British are barbarians. As we leave the patient's bedside he says "we turn him on other side in two hours time" and I note that it is now 10 am. We go down the row of patients and it's the same careful and gentle approach with each one of them.

Next John asks me to help him with the patient who I saw on the veranda and felt that he was near death. He has screened the bed off to give the patient some privacy. I doubt that in the state the patient is in he is worried about privacy but it is not just about his possible embarrassment it is also about us showing compassion and giving dignity to those we are entrusted to care for. I have just read a book called "On the edge of the Primeval Forest" by Albert Schweitzer, doctor and missionary. He put it in a nutshell when he said that the primary ethic from which all other ethics spring, is reverence for life. That's what this job is really all about, reverence for life and it should not make any difference if a person is disfigured, unattractive or even repugnant.

As I look at the patient I see a small bundle of contracted limbs. A remnant piece of terminally ill humanity. A bag of bones and tightly stretched translucent skin. At some point he was a young fit person like me but now the spirit of life is ebbing away. His fixed cold large black glazed eyes look out from sunken sockets. His mouth is stretched open like something on a fishmonger's slab. Only the shallow almost imperceptible hiss of his breath and the laboured rise and fall of his bony white chest confirm that life is still present. I can only wonder why the struggle for life goes on when there is neither hope nor purpose, but the heart beats on and the suffering continues and life for now endures.

We have to handle the little patient very gently as we change his bed. He is so emaciated he must only weigh about three or four stone. His leg muscles are so contracted that his heels touch his buttocks and his knees almost touch his chin. I see that he also has a marked curvature of his spine. When we finish changing him John puts a urine bottle between his legs and gently places a knitted wool square over his shoulders to keep him warm.

My next task with John is to observe the old patients who do ward worker given their weekly pay. We both have to countersign the payment records to ensure that the patients have received their money. The patients dutifully line up at the office door to receive from the deputy charge nurse a few pounds, shillings and pence. John and I stare over the deputy's shoulder as he puts his signature next to each patient's name. When the last one has left John and I sign in the appropriate column to verify that the money has been paid out. I have heard from some of the staff that the deputy retrieves some of the money from the less able patients. They say he knows exactly where each patient puts his money and which patients will be compliant if he asks for it back. It certainly wouldn't surprise me if all of this was true. The deputy then instructs John and me to go to first lunch. We don't need telling twice as we quickly wash our hands and head for the door.

Although its not good practice to do strenuous exercise after eating, I join staff nurse Dave Johnson for a weight lifting session in a room we have obtained off the main corridor. Upon return to the ward I watch the deputy leave for his lunch and decide to see if the patients still have their money. Touchy and old Tom still have theirs but despite asking the others and looking under their pillows and mattresses I fail to trace any of the money and I wonder if John and I were deliberately sent to first lunch to clear the coast for the deputy to get the money back. Maybe there is another explanation, maybe what I have heard are just malicious rumours, or maybe I'm just being too suspicious.

During the afternoon visitors start to arrive. There are two types of patient in this ward, those who have grown old in this hospital and those who have led normal lives until old age has robbed them of their faculties and independence. You can almost tell with certainty which patients have grown old in hospital because in most instances they have no visitors and have been abandoned many years ago. It's the usual event of cakes and sweet stuffing time. God knows what will lurk below those crisp white sheets and counterpanes this evening when we start our bed changing round. Those patients who have been stuffed with fruit will be in the worst state and in some cases the diarrhoea will last for several days.

As the visiting continues the deputy charge nurse, with his pencil thin moustache, looks like a poor man's version of Errol Flynn. He's floating around the visitors especially the young or attractive women. I have seen it all before and feel slightly amused by his performance.

After the visitors have left we set for tea. I doubt if some of the patients will have any room left for more food. Then after tea it's time for one of us to collect all the false teeth for cleaning and overnight storage. It is not an easy job retrieving dentures from the patient's mouths. It takes a deft hand movement to get them out quickly before you get bitten. Once out you put the teeth into individually named jars then take them into the backs and clean them all. As there are about 30 sets of teeth this is not the nicest of jobs. Luckily it is not my task this time. It is another student who Jim calls The Mouth. He is loud, brash and rough with the patients, especially when changing them if they are resistive. I have seen him rip the shirts off patient's backs to avoid having to undo the buttons. Having accomplished the task of collecting the teeth he is walking towards me up the aisle between the beds. Suddenly he trips and staggers forward discharging the contents of his tray all over the floor. There are jars and teeth scattered everywhere. I hear the deputy shout "Christ, what are you doing" as I move to help him. Once we get all the teeth back on the tray we realise that we have no way of establishing which teeth belong to which patient. John Pali has come on the scene and looks aghast at the pile of teeth. In broken English he says "You make mess, you stupid, you go clean them now" When "The Mouth" returns he looks more subdued than I have ever seen him. There is now no other way to establish whose teeth are whose than to try every set in every patient's mouth. Even then there is no guarantee that we will get it right as some of the patients dentures have always been ill-fitting. It's an awful task and the thought of putting 30 pairs of someone else's teeth into a patient's mouth is revolting. It also means that while we are attempting to do this one of us has to hold both of the struggling patient's hands while the other tries to get his mouth open more than twenty times to put the teeth in and out. The task gets easier and quicker as we manage to identify each most suitable set of teeth. I say most suitable because I know we will not get it right every time. I sense that John is quietly fuming but he says nothing. It takes the three of us until the night staff come on at 7.30 pm to finish the job.

Two weeks have passed, it's just another day of routine and lunch has just finished. There is a temporary lull in activity and two nurses have decided to play a prank on a group of old patients still sitting at the dinner table. From the office they have filled syringes with water and are squirting these patients through the gap in the door. One of the patients is a stocky old farmer in a tweed suit. When the jet hits him full in the face he shouts out and swings his walking stick around his head narrowly missing the other patients sitting at the table. The old man doesn't know where the water is coming from and the nurses stifle their laughter in case they give their position away. This is repeated several times and the old farmer is getting into quite a lather. One of the nurses says to me "You have a go" and I fill a syringe from the sink. Aiming the syringe I squirt another old patient in the back of his neck and the water runs down his collar. He too shouts out a few swear words and swings his arms about. As soon as I have done this I realise that this type of so called joke may be judged by some as harmless fun but I realise that it is the start of a long steep slope that can eventually lead to abuse. I feel very ashamed of myself and put the syringes down and walk away. This is a salutary lesson for me as I have always thought that I would never stoop this low, but now I know just how easy it is to become involved in something as unsavoury as this. I vow "Never again. Never ever."

Time has passed and Jimmy Herons the large charge nurse has been in charge for these last two weeks. After tea he takes me to one of the locked store cupboards and beckons me to go inside. The cupboard is stacked with empty lemonade and Tizer bottles that relatives have brought in for the patients. He orders "Collect all those empty lemonade bottles and put them in the back of my car." He notices my slightly puzzled look and explains that he will take them all to the corner shop and get the two penny deposit for each bottle. I presume the money is for his own pocket. I do not think he considers this as theft because the bottles if left would only be dumped with the rubbish. His car is parked outside the ward and it takes me several journeys to fill up the boot and the back seats. This exercise reminds me of the scorched earth policy practiced during the second world. I have seen it in many similar forms here. Those with the power commandeer everything of value and leave nothing behind.

At the end of the shift I watch Jimmy squeeze into his Ford Popular with his chest and great belly pushed within a fraction of the steering wheel. The sight of his huge bulk driving away with a large stash of bottles aboard would be the best possible advert for a Ford car's suspension and the durability of it's engines.

I have been on this ward now for several weeks and next week I am going on nights but not on another ward; unfortunately I am staying here. I have finished the morning wet round with another nurse. Old Jim the ward worker is in bed with a bad chest infection. His job of emptying the urine bottles and sputum mugs has been given to me. As I walk towards the veranda door I see that the terminally ill patient is lying naked at the bottom of his unscreened bed in full view of the other patients. The two nurses attending to him are changing the bed from the top not from the side. Having put the clean sheet on the bottom of the bed they have moved him on to it to enable them to make the top and change the pillow cases. This is fine as it's done this way to avoid having to roll a patient painfully from side to side. However you should keep the patient covered at all times; that's doubly important here as the veranda is freezing cold. I wander up the line of beds collecting the urine bottles and on my way back I pass the bed again. The patient looks like a contorted white bag of bones and he is still naked. The two nurses have finished the top of the bed and they pick him up under his arms and knees and swing him backwards and forwards as if he was on a swing. At the end of the momentum they let him go in mid air and he lands at the top of the bed. As he lands one nurse exclaims "Christ he's gone" and as I look he appears to have died. The other nurse replies "Best thing for the old bugger." His death is confirmed by stethoscope and the doctor is then informed. So ends another person's life. I only hope that when I get old I am not confined in my last days to a place like this.

When I came on this morning I saw the staff nurses and the charge nurse in a huddle and I wondered what was going on but thought no more of it and got on with the work. The news has now broken. A student that I know was on duty here last night. Apparently while the other nurse was away on his break the student was sitting in an armchair when he was attacked from behind by one of our old patients. The patient had hit him over the head with a pair of long heavy metal cheetle forceps that are used for lifting bowls out of the sterilizer. The first blow had not knocked the student out but apparently the patient continued to rain blows down on his head. With considerable effort the student who was quite fit and powerfully built was able to fend the patient off and ultimately overpower him. The student had sustained several deep lacerations to his scalp. When help finally arrived the nurses who went to his assistance said the student's head and white coat were covered in blood. The charge nurse says he is expected to be off work for some time. I would never have thought that such a very old patient would be able to mount such a sustained attack. It seems that some very old patients here are totally unpredictable and capable of considerable violence.

I've been on nights a week now and surprisingly I am quite enjoying it. I am working with a good staff nurse and almost everything is done by the book. The exception is medication. He has two dodgy practices that I feel other staff on permanent nights may also practice. The first is to put a handful of Sodium Barbitone 3 grain tablets in his white coat pocket and as he goes around the beds he drops one into the open mouths of any patient he knows from experience can be restless or noisy. There is no way the pharmacy can check the overall number of tablets that are being used as they are issued in large stock bottles containing several hundred tablets. The other practice which I know also happens on other wards, is to dish out to fractious patients more than the prescribed amount of paraldehyde. To cover this practice up the nurse adds an equal the amount of water to the paraldehyde bottle. The only problem is that if this is overdone what's left in the bottle becomes so diluted that it is almost useless. The attitude is one of who cares, that's someone else's problem further on in the week.

I have just received a phone call that Doctor Latner is on her way to see a patient and it's just my luck that the staff nurse is on his break. Dr Latner is a very attractive rather fiery redhead. She is a brilliant doctor with very high standards and she does not tolerate slack practices. I scoot round the beds quickly and tidy up, removing any full urine bottles. Just as I finish I hear the key in the door and within seconds she is standing in front of me. Immediately she sees that I have placed a row of mobile screens in front of the office windows. "Why are the screens there, how can you see the patients" she asks in a rather accusing tone. I explain that I always sit outside the office so that I can both see and hear the patients and that the screens are to shield the patients from the office lights so their sleep is not disturbed. I also tell her that to keep the noise down I wear gym shoes at night. She continues for a few seconds to look thoughtfully and disapprovingly at the screens, then she smiles and says "that sounds reasonable, they can stay there." I breathe a sigh of relief when she finishes her work and finally leaves the ward; apparently she is satisfied with everything. When the staff nurse returns from supper I inform him that Dr Latner has been and give him an account of what has happened. He seems more than happy that he has missed her. It's now my turn to leave the ward and as I walk towards the staff café I hope that there will be someone to talk to. Unfortunately I eat my supper alone as the mess room is empty apart from two older female nurses sitting and talking quietly at the far side of the room. Both are unknown to me.

Making my way back to the ward I go down the dark link corridor off the main corridor. At the bottom of the corridor I hear a slight noise to my right. I stop and in the darkness I can just see the shape of someone crouching at a door to the female ward. Curious, I press myself to the wall and stand silently until the figure straightens up, takes a few steps back and then goes up the stairs to another ward. Its Cowell the Owl, the night superintendent. Jim started calling him Cowell the Owl as he has a very white face, a pointed nose and two deep sunken black eyes and he is on permanent night duty. What's he been looking at? I wait for a moment to ensure that he has completely gone and then approach the door. Bending down I look through the key hole. Sitting facing the door I see a female nurse reading a book with her feet towards me up on a desk. The way she is sitting allows me to see almost to the top of her legs. Hastily I stand up and move away from the door. So that's his game, he's a Peeping Tom, the dirty old bugger. I wonder how long he's being doing this and what else he gets up to on nights. As I return to the ward I chuckle to myself quietly. Who would think that of old Cowell the Owl?

Two weeks have passed since my encounter with the Owl and tonight is my last night duty. The staff nurse has gone to first supper again leaving me alone on the ward. The ward is in darkness and most of the patients are asleep. Suddenly the phone rings and it's Dr Latner again. She tells me that she is coming to the ward in a few minutes to examine a new patient who came in today. Finishing the conversation I put the phone down. This is the second time I have been on my own to deal with Dr Latner. I wonder if the staff nurse has some way of knowing when she is coming. Maybe the information was given to him at handover from the day staff. I leg it quickly down to the clinical room and scurry around setting up a suitable trolley with stethoscope, blood pressure machine, thermometer, aurascope, patella hammer etc. Leaving the clinical room I ensure that everything is in order around the new patient's bed. In the gloom towards the back of the ward I see Old Tom working his way up the aisle towards me emptying the urine bottles into his bucket. Nipping back to the clinical room I retrieve my completed trolley and push it towards the new patient's bed. As I approach my left foot goes into the bucket full of urine that Old Tom has placed unseen at the side of the bed. My foot has wedged in the bottom of the bucket and for a moment I am hopping unsteadily with it on the end of my foot. As I try to extricate it I lose my balance but just manage to clutch the bed rail to stop me from falling. My foot is then released from the bucket and it tips over spilling all its foul contents over the floor and under the new patient's bed. My trouser leg, sock and shoe are soaked with urine and the smell all around the beds is vile. Under my breath I curse my bad luck. As I run to find a mop old Tom is nowhere to be seen; just as well because I might strangle him. Mopping the floor takes an age as the urine has gone under a number of beds and soaked several pairs of patients slippers. Once I have got most of it up I pour a full bottle of strong smelling disinfectant on the floor. Just as I ponder how I am going to eradicate the dreadful smell coming from my trouser leg, sock and shoe I hear a key in the lock followed by the characteristic sound of high heels on lino. My luck is certainly not in tonight. All I needed was another fifteen minutes and I would have made sure that no one could have detected what had taken place. I realise it's too late now as her diminutive figure appears in the dormitory doorway, her pristine white coat contrasting sharply with her bright red hair and well applied makeup. There's nothing else for it, I will have to tell her what has happened. As she listens I can see a slight expression of sympathy pass across her face. She looks down at my wet trouser, sticking tightly to my leg. She shows her distaste of the smell by wrinkling her nose and says "what are you going to do about your trousers and shoes." I reply that I will have to ask permission to borrow some clothes from the ward stocks and return them tomorrow. Indicating that this is a good idea she says that I should get on with it and that she will be able to examine the patient without my help. I manage to find a pair of trousers that are unfortunately a bit short and a pair of clean woollen socks that are as stiff as a board. from previously been boiled in the laundry. However Beggars cannot be choosers! When Dr Latner finishes the examination she scribbles a few notes and then gives me a cheery good night. I bet she tells all her doctor friends about tonight and I'm sure they all have a good laugh. For me, well I might have bad luck sometimes but despite this I feel I usually come up smelling of roses. Well, not precisely in this instance.

I have just heard that Enoch Powell, Minister of Health has delivered a report following his whistle-stop tour of mental hospitals. It's being referred to as the water tower report, as one of the distinctive landmarks in most psychiatric hospitals is a water tower. Apparently he has said that the government will close all of the large Victorian Hospitals in fifteen years, that's about in 1976. What a laugh, there is no way this is going to happen. He can make these promises easily because he won't be Minister of Health by then and the Conservative Party may not even be the ruling party. While I agree wholeheartedly with his sentiments and his objective I know he has no chance of achieving the closures anywhere near his declared the time scale. It's just another case of political pie in the sky.

CHAPTER 7.

QUALIFIED AT LAST

Its now July 1962 and 12 months have passed since I worked with Jim on Larry Docherty's ward. It's been a year of mixed fortunes. I passed my final examinations in March and have now reached the dizzy heights of becoming a State Registered Mental Nurse. (RMN), Jim has passed a chiropody correspondence course and has left the hospital to take up a post as a chiropodist in a large department store in Newcastle city centre. Although I still see him quite a lot socially I have missed his presence at work. Vince has also left and taken his small son to live with him in London. I also miss his friendship and unfortunately I have lost his address and am unable to make further contact with him.

As I think back over the last three months since qualifying I recall a number of interesting and rather unusual experiences. The first took place when I was a staff nurse on night duty alone and in charge of Ward 20, the Refractory Ward. The experience was quite frightening even though the most violent patients were locked in the strong rooms. After I had given out the medication and turned the lights off I settled down at my table in the dormitory. The only light in the dark dormitory was from my heavily shaded angle-poise lamp. My chair was between two patients beds. Hoping for a quite night I had picked up a book and started to read. The ward was quiet and I began to relax. Suddenly one of the patient next to me sat up in bed and gave a loud piercing scream. I nearly hit the roof with shock and I felt as if my heart had jumped into my mouth. Then just as quickly he lay down again without a murmur. It took several minutes for my heart rate to get back to normal and for me to regain my composure. As I started to read again, at the top of the row of beds I heard Buster shout across the ward to another patient that he had been home at the weekend. "I have seen my girl friend this weekend" he announced with some pride. The reply he got from another patient on the opposite side of the ward was mocking "Ger on you've never had a girl friend." "Yes I have" he retorted in a voice that appeared to lack a certain amount of conviction. "Nar yer hav'nt who are you kiddin." That was all it needed. Buster was out of his bed like a shot and lumbered across the room and started throwing wild punches at the head of his antagonist. In self protection the other patient put his head under the pillow and pulled the blankets over his head. Other patients aroused from their slumbers by the commotion sat up and became interested spectators. At this point the other patient lost his rag and jumped out of bed to face his assailant. They stood toe to toe swapping ungainly but heavy blows to the head and body. For me this was really nerve racking. The phone was a few yards away but there was no guarantee that it would be answered and the night deputy's ward round was at least an hour away. If I intervened these two guys would make mincemeat of me so I sat tight and watched the fight. After a while I could see they were tiring and the blows became more laboured. At the point when I could see that they had almost fought themselves to a standstill I got up from my chair and walked down the central aisle between the beds towards them. Gathering myself to my full height I commanded the loudest and deepest voice I could muster. "That's it, that's enough, get back to bed, - Now!" To my utter surprise without a word in response, they both meekly ran to their beds and pulled the blankets over their heads. As I turned and walked back to my chair the patients each lay back down like a line of falling dominoes and there was complete silence as I dipped my angle poise lamp, plunging the ward into almost total darkness. As I sat there I could hardly believe how fortunate I had been. It certainly was a lucky outcome. Things could easily have turned out badly. The rest of the night was uneventful and I didn't hear a squeak from anyone until the morning. I was thankful that I was off duty the following night.

What I didn't know until later was that the following night a very old nurse took over from me. During his first night on duty three patients intent on escape threatened him. Apparently as they were engaged in tearing the telephone off the wall he was able to escape their clutches and get out of the ward and run for help. The three patients made their exit by ripping off toilet seats and using them to smash their way through the Georgian framed rear toilet window and shinning down the drainpipe.

The second incident took place on the ward while I was off duty. A recently admitted patient ran across the ward day room and using the leather sofa like a trampoline vaulted through the first floor window, taking the entire wooden frame and glass with him. He was very lucky to miss the concrete path below and fall on rain soaked earth. Amazingly he only broke one of his legs. I don't know what might have prompted him to do this, but I asked myself was it his mental state? or had he been on the receiving end of the charge nurses brutal admission procedures? I shall never know.

The third incident was a long and anxiety provoking experience. It took place during a period on night duty when I was working on Ward 16, the ward that Jim had named Dockerty's Ducks Having settled the patients down for the night I had sat down at my table in the dormitory to read a book. After about an hour, out of the corner of my eye I caught sight of something dark on the floor creeping towards me. Looking more intently I saw that a pool of water was forming under my table near to my feet. I leapt up in alarm and saw a stream of water flowing down from the bathroom at the far end of the dormitory. As I ran up the aisle between the beds the further I went the deeper the water got. As soon as I opened the heavy wooden door to the bathroom I could hear the rush of water. Getting to the bath I saw that it was overflowing and that both taps were running full bore. The reason for the flood was that paper had been stuffed down the plughole. With some effort I managed to turn the taps off but to reach the plug hole I had to press up against the bath and put the full length of my arm into the full bath, getting soaked in the process. At this moment two patients came wading in with their pyjama trouser bottoms soaking wet. With a few well chosen words I managed to turn them round and usher them back into the dormitory. In the dormitory several other patients were paddling about as if they were walking along the sea shore. As fast as I got them back to bed others sprang up. I was in a total panic; this was an upstairs ward and the sick ward was below. Not only that but the night superintendent was due on his round in about two hours time. There would be hell to pay if he saw the mess. The only option I had was to get all the blankets out of the store and try to mop up the water that was by then about an inch and a half deep across the full length and width of the bathroom and dormitory. First I threw all of the blankets onto the floor and then one by one tried to wring the sodden things out into the bath. Trying to wring out a heavy woollen blanket was a strenuous and difficult task rather like wrestling with a python. An hour into the task and it looked no better, the place was still awash. I was frazzled and soaking wet. After a further half hour I could see that I was winning. After two hours I had got all of the water up and the heating was drying the floor nicely. Unbelievably I hadn't received any phone calls from the ward below so the water must not have penetrated through the floor. I dumped all the wet blankets in the bath and changed into a clean white coat. Ten minutes later I had heard the night super's key in the lock. To conceal anything that might have given the situation away I kept my angle- poise light shade well down within an inch of my table, the effect of which kept the dormitory quite dark. Sitting at my table looking alert and composed I stood up as the night superintendent entered. As he strode quickly towards me he asked "Is everything alright?" Yes I replied it's quiet and everything is fine. Without another word he made his exit by the bottom door and I gave a big sigh of relief. I definitely do lead a charmed life. If he had seen the flood his first conclusion would have been that I had been asleep on duty.

Over this period I had also worked for a few nights in the office in charge of the night shift. The rapid transition from being a student to being in charge of the entire hospital was quite daunting but luckily there were no problems and everything went smoothly.

Also over this last year I have sensed that I had become something of a "blue eyed boy" to Mr Gibbons the chief male nurse. My first inkling came when out of the blue he asked me if I would join the social club committee. This was a new experience for me as I had never sat on a committee before. Once I got used to this new experience I suggested to the committee that we should start a rambling club. The idea rapidly caught on and soon became a great success. We had about twenty members and we did long treks up to about 15 miles across country to places like Kielder Forest and the Yorkshire Moors. Jim named the club the Whoring Touring Club as during the walks pairs of people kept disappearing into the bushes only to emerge hours later at the final destination, which was usually a pub. Another venture was an attempt to walk 110 miles non-stop from Edinburgh to Newcastle for a cancer charity. There was no planning, no training and it was a disaster from start to finish. We arrived in snowbound Edinburgh train station at about 8 pm on the coldest night in Scotland since the mid eighteen hundreds. Our escort car with supplies of food, drinks and dry clothes had been there for several hours. The plan, such as it was, was for four of us to set off and the car to catch us up after three hours and supply us with food and clean socks. We left Edinburgh at 9.30pm and covered about 12 miles in 3 hours with no sign of the escort car. Once in open county it was pitch black and the temperature was sub zero. The snow ploughs had been out piling up snow about five feet high on both sides of the road. It was like walking in a sledge run. The surface of the road was compacted with snow covered ice and we kept slipping and falling. The only way we could keep our balance was to walk in single file with our right foot in the powdered snow at the edge of the road. One consequence of this was that if someone at the front fell, we all went down heavily like a pack of cards. Another consequence was that our right foot and leg got soaking wet from being immersed up to the calf in snow. After walking like this for four hours at a painfully slow pace we saw the escort car approaching. We weren't too happy with the occupants but we gratefully changed our wet socks and waited eagerly for the primus to heat the soup. Unfortunately the first mouthful I took burnt my mouth and tongue which didn't reduce my sense of exasperation with the whole disorganised venture. Worse was to follow when someone saw steam rising from under the car engine. After lifting the bonnet and unscrewing the radiator cap we saw that the radiator was empty. The next hour was spent heating snow on the primus stove to fill the radiator. When this was finally accomplished lo and behold we found that the car was stuck in the snow. This time we decided that it was necessary for the car to go ahead of us for about ten miles and then wait for us to catch up. Getting the car out of the drift used up a lot of what little energy we had left but we did finally succeed and stood and watched with some anxiety as it sped off into the night. As we trudged on, cold and dispirited, five miles came and went, then ten miles came and went and then fifteen. I and two others were totally exhausted and incapable of going much further. Our feet were frozen and wet and we had developed some painful blisters. We openly cursed the car driver and co-driver for bungling their part of the plan to support us. When we did finally reach them a few choice words were exchanged and we declared that we were packing it in. As we bundled ourselves into the cramped back seat our fourth compatriot said he was going to walk on, so we let him go having agreed to wait two hours before going to catch him up. After two hours we set off but all we could see was mile after mile of white landscape. Then suddenly I said "stop I'm sure I saw someone back there." As we backed slowly down the road I saw his rigid lanky frame sitting motionless on a wall. He hadn't even waved to us. As we waded through deep snow towards him he didn't move but he was able to say he couldn't get down off the wall or walk. So we carried him back to the car still in a sitting position. As he started to thaw out he began to cry with the pain. Had he been left any longer on that wall the consequences could have been serious. Needless to say we didn't collect any money for our charity but we later did a second successful non-stop walk of 50 miles from Berwick-on-Tweed to Newcastle.

The second reason for me thinking I had become one of Mr Gibbons "blue eyed boys" was later when he chose me to accompany him and his wife to return a Polish patient to Bangor Hospital near Edinburgh. It seemed an endless journey as I had to sit for nearly 3 hours in the back of the car with a mute patient. Still, tea with dainty crust free sandwiches served on a silver tray in Matron's apartment was rather nice but somewhat daunting as I felt like a fish out of water trying to engage in small talk in the company of such elevated people. One incident during our return journey stuck in my mind. It was when Mr Gibbons announced that it was time for a some "light relief." At a lay-by we stopped and he and I went into a pine forest at the side of the road. The trees were very young and the trunks were only about a foot in diameter. Strangely we both chose the same tree him on one side and me on the other. From my side I could see both of his shoulders and both of his legs but not his head or his other vital parts. I found it difficult to concentrate on the job in hand due to the sound of running water and small cloud of steam rising from the other side of the tree. You have to realise that Mr Gibbons was called God by the nurses. I saw him as a mortal but one on a very high pedestal. For him and me to be performing such a basic function so close together seemed rather surreal but it also appealed to my rather quirky sense of humour.

My worst experiences during this period was a trip to the circus on the Town Moor. The circus had given the hospital a number of complimentary tickets for the opening night which we were told was going to be televised.

The names of the staff accompanying patients had been posted on the corridor notice board. The first thing I noticed was that most staff had been allocated 4 or 5 patients. When I came to my name I saw that I had been allocated only one. My first reaction was that it was my blue eyes again, that was until I saw the name of the patient. It was the big Irishman Buster from the Refractory Ward. I knew immediately that this was going to be a nightmare experience.

When he day of the circus arrived I made my way to Ward 20. Buster spotted me immediately as I walked through the day room and came loping towards me. "I'm going to the circus, I'm going to the circus. Do you like my new coat." He could hardly contain himself and although he was a big man his new coat almost came down to his ankles. As we set off down the ward corridor he eagerly ran ahead. Out in the hospital drive I had to run to keep up with him. At the bus stop he loudly told every passer-by that he was going to the circus. Some looked quite startled by his sudden and loud approach and increased their pace to get away as quickly as possible. When the bus arrived he shot up the stairs to the crowded upper deck. Unfortunately for me there were only two seats, one at the very front which he commandeered and one at the back which I occupied. As the bus started off he kept shouting to all and sundry "I'm going to the circus" and then turning round to me to shout down the aisle "that's right isn't it, we are going to the circus." Talk about being embarrassed. On several occasions during the journey he ran down the aisle to speak to me and only after some persuasion went back to his seat.

This was the first time I had been outside the hospital with a patient and of course it had to be one of the biggest and most difficult to control. There was always the prospect that he would run off and I knew that there was no way I could force him to return to hospital. It was nerve racking. I was slightly relieved when we finally got off the bus but as we did he bolted ahead to cross the busy road. I just managed to catch him and hold on to him. Once across the road we tramped across the grass and arrived at the circus tent. There was a large queue milling about outside the entrance and we took our place at the back behind two young women. As people piled in behind us we were pushed forward until we were uncomfortably close to the two young women. However no such discomfort for Buster; he was in his element. He gave me a nudge and a meaningful look; he had spotted the two shapely posteriors in front of him and was making grasping gestures with both hands towards his intended targets. I had no option but to say forcefully to him "DON'T, NO DON'T. He looked at me a bit sheepishly but thankfully he had got the message but he still kept glancing towards the objects of his desire. Finally the doors opened and, clutching our complimentary tickets, we surged forward. In the process I managed to separate us from the two young women in front which gave me a profound feeling of relief. Once in the tent he was off again with me trying to keep close behind him. He eventually found a seat on a wooden bench about six rows back from the ring. The rows behind us then began to fill up. Suddenly he twisted round and shouted out loudly "Get your bloody feet off my new coat" As I turned I saw that his long coat had overlapped the wooden bench and was trailing on the floor and that the man sitting behind him had inadvertently trodden on it. The man looked petrified as Buster raised his fist and I just managed to dissuade him from letting fly. A few moments later the band struck up and the Ring Master entered, resplendent in his red coat, top hat and whip. Across the ring I could see the TV cameraman æroing in for the action to begin. This totally distracted Buster and he turned round to watch the show. For the rest of the time he paid rapt attention. He especially showed his appreciation of the scantily dressed circus girls by clapping and cheering them loudly. For the first time I felt able to relax but in the back of my mind I was not looking forward to the bus journey back. Then the Ringmaster re-entered the ring and announced that he would pay £5 to anyone who could ride the unrideable horse. In a split second Buster was on his feet with one arm raised in the air. With more than a bit of luck I managed to grab the back of his coat and hold on. He turned towards me angrily and shouted "I want to ride it, let me ride the horse." I could visualise the TV cameras turning towards us. In these circumstances I certainly did not fancy even briefly appearing on TV. If he had managed to break free god knows what I would have done. Suddenly he stopped pulling away from me and sat down saying "I can get £5 pounds, "I can get £5" I responded by firmly saying "No" and remarkably he accepted it. We continued to watch the show as a number of circus men masquerading as members of the audience tried to mount the horse. All failed miserably but it was a great laugh. Buster loved it but kept on insisting that he could do better. The rest of the show passed without incident and during the bus journey home Buster was remarkably quiet. As I delivered him safely back to the ward I thought to myself never again. At the time I wondered who on earth gave me that assignment, they should have known it was fraught with possible problems. I would have liked to have known on what basis the decision was made to send a refractory patient like Buster out at night with a single escort.

CHAPTER 8.

THE END OF THE BEGINNING

I have just been given some great news by one of the managers. Myself and three other male staff nurses who I have trained with are being sent on a 2 year secondment to do our general hospital training. Up until now newly qualified staff have had to wait three or four years before being seconded. I am not sure why it has only taken us a year, it could be that some nurses have turned down the opportunity. General training is considered by those who have undertaken it to be very hard work and a daunting experience. I am really chuffed because those who obtain dual qualifications are held in very high regard. To be a Registered Mental Nurse (RMN) and a Registered General Nurse (SRN) would be a great achievement and the other good news is that while I am doing this further training I will continue to receive my full staff nurse's salary.

It's now the week before I am due to leave with three friends, Tony Coxon, Keith Davies and Arthur Brown to become a post registered student at Newcastle General Hospital. I have heard that at least one of my three colleagues has reservations about having female ward sisters as bosses. Up until now we have only worked with men in charge.

Nurses seconded in previous years have made disparaging remarks about petticoat managers. However they have also acknowledged that the Matron and ward sisters really know every aspect of their jobs. Having worked with some of the male charge nurses here I am quite looking forward to working under the direction of female managers. It could be like a breath of fresh air. I am not really bothered if they are very autocratic, I am going to learn new skills not to judge a popularity contest.

The charge nurse has informed me that I have been called to the Chief Male Nurse's office. As I walk down the corridor I wonder why he wants to see me. On arriving at his office door I hesitate for a moment then give it a gentle tap to indicate my presence. I hear him call out "Come in." As I enter he is sitting at his desk looking very impressive and dignified in his smart suit and well trimmed thick wavy grey hair. He gives me a warm smile and beckons me towards a chair. He then fixes me with his steely blue eyes that make me feel uncomfortable. It's as if he can read my thoughts but in reality I know in many ways he has difficulty seeing beyond his nose end. He is a pleasant gentleman who is a very good figurehead but one who appears to be oblivious to many of the things going on around him. He clears his throat and says "I just wanted to see you to wish you good luck with your general training." He then adds "and I should warn you that general hospitals are full of very sexy young female nurses." I smile in response but feel it's a slightly incongruous thing to say to me and wonder what prompted it. Is this a standard comment he makes to all male secondees, based on his personal experience in general hospitals? Or is it some sort of veiled warning? Or could it be a perverse subtle incentive? I cannot even guess. We then talk about my obligation to return after two years at the completion of my general training and I assure him that it is my firm intension. The conversation ends there and he stands up and extends his right hand towards me. I shake it warmly and turn and leave the office.

My final week has passed quickly and as I walk down the long drive having completed my last shift I feel rather sad at leaving behind the patients and staff I have got to know so well. Its been a wonderful contrasting five years, a uneasy mixture of great camaraderie, humour, sadness, loathing and despair. I have learned some stark lessons about the dark side of human nature and how some male nurses are more akin to devils than angels whilst other nurses working under the same conditions and restraints are kind and compassionate. Possibly more than this I have learned a lot about myself and my strengths and maybe mostly about my weaknesses but the experience overall has engendered in me a sense of optimism and a strong determination to work towards ending the endemic institutional cruelty to patients. In future years along with other good nurses I hope to play a small part in this process. Although it seems fanciful to even think about it now, I have promised myself that one day I will write the story of what it has been like here, not so much about the good nurses of whom there are many but about the bad apples who are ill treating mentally ill people with impunity. I have also vowed that in the future I will always be honest and truthful about my training and work in this hospital and as uncomfortable as it will be I will always speak truthfully about how I failed to defend some of the patients in our care.

After this weekend I will be starting work at Newcastle General Hospital and thinking about this I feel a mixture of apprehension tinged with excitement. Working on surgical and children's wards and in the operating theatres sounds very challenging. I can hardly wait to start my new adventure.

CHAPTER 9.

THE NEW BEGINNING

Its 1965 and two years have now passed and I have finished my general nurse training. Although I have sat my final examinations I will have to wait six weeks before I know if I have passed. Just before I left the general hospital the matron, Matron Shaw, offered me the post of Charge Nurse in the Professorial Department of Psychological Medicine if I passed the exams. I was amazed to be offered such a prestigious post so early in my career. Back at the Psychiatric Hospital I would have had to wait many years even to become a Deputy Charge Nurse and many more years to become a Charge Nurse.

I have thoroughly enjoyed the last two years as a student in this General Hospital and the time has past relatively quickly. It has been a great experience and I have gained knowledge in several specialities, cardiovascular, urology, medicine, surgery, operating theatre, neurology and paediatrics. But it hasn't all been about learning new skills.

Mr Gibbons the chief male nurse was dead right when he said at my leaving interview that there would be many beautiful sexy young nurses in this hospital. I had hardly set foot in the place before it began. During my first placement in urology the pretty young ward sister constantly flirted with me despite the fact that she was soon to get married She first surprised me by showing me the full extent of her black nylon clad legs with a frilly red and black garters around her thighs. She was vivacious and full of fun. On the same ward alone in the clinical room I was directly propositioned by an older married nursing assistant who said her husband had lost interest in her. There was also a lovely dark haired young student I worked with at night on paediatrics. She had a combination of intelligence and shyness mixed with a hint of devilishness and daring. She was reputed to have a boy friend who was a rugby player so I had no wish to be tackled by him. It was therefore literally just a case of two ships that passed silently in the night. Again on nights in neurology there was a very provocative staff nurse who had only been introduced to me the night before. She tried to lure me into an empty side room. I found out later that she was leaving and that the night in question was her last night at the hospital. My friend told me she was a bible puncher who was a member of the Salvation Army. I certainly think she had more than saving me on her mind. Last but not least was a young blonde student who came on strongly despite being the girlfriend of my best friend. They all knew I was married but it did not seem to curtail their amorous intentions in fact it appeared to spur them on. Working in a General Hospital has been in marked contrast with the almost monastic environment of the wards back in the Bin. Being in a situation where women are predominant certainly helps to spice up working life. Who says nurses are angels.

Reflecting further on the Matron's offer of a charge nurse's post I wonder if an incident that happened during my first month at the general hospital had anything to do with it. It was when I was working on a rain soaked day in the clinical room of men's urology ward. It was early morning and as I was cleaning syringes I glanced out of the window that overlooked the hospital perimeter wall. On the other side of the wall at the far corner of a lane I could see a large shaggy dog standing motionless in the pelting rain. I thought no more about it until near the end of my shift when I again looked out of the window and saw that the dog was still there looking soaked and forlorn. So when I left the ward I decided to round to the back of the hospital to see if the dog to see if it had a name tag on. The rain was still lashing down and the dog didn't move as I approached it. I fumbled around its neck to find its name tag amongst its wet matted coat. It had one and the address on the tag was for a street about quarter of a mile away. The main problem was that I had no lead, no rope or string and there was no way it was going to follow me, especially across a main road. The duffle coat I was wearing was already quite wet but I had no choice but to pick the dog up and clutch its heavy body to my chest. The result was like squeezing a sponge. The water poured out of the dogs coat and ran down my front and down my trousers and into my shoes as I staggered off in the direction of its home. By the time I reached the large Victorian house I was like a drowned rat. On the plus side however was the fact that the dog had been quite docile and hadn't struggled or tried to bite me. I rang the door bell still clutching the dog to my chest. I stood there dripping wet with my hair plastered all over my face. I seemed to wait for ages. I began to wonder if the person was out but finally the door opened and a middle aged lady emerged and guess who it was, it was Matron Shaw. To add to the surprise was the fact that her uniform dress was fully unbuttoned at the top exposing her ample bra. This state of exposure was never how we expected to see Matron but she seemed quite oblivious of her half undressed state. She was obviously preoccupied and delighted to see her dog. She said it was quite old and partly blind. I explained that I was a post registered student at the hospital and how I had found her dog. In return she thanked me profusely and said how pleased she was to have the dog safely back home. Maybe as 2 years have now passed since this incident she may have forgotten about me and the dog rescue or maybe returning her dog had tipped the balance in favour of my possible promotion. I shall never know.

Its my first day back at the old Psychiatric Hospital or Old Bin as we call it. It's a strange feeling to be walking back up the main drive after such a long time. Its quite nostalgic. An old long stay patient who I know well is shuffling down the path towards me. He stops in front of me and says " I haven't seen you for a while, have you been on holiday?" I hear myself say "yes" as I pat him on the shoulder. Before I left the hospital two years ago I used to see him at least once a day in the corridors. I've always felt that time has little or no meaning for many of the patients here and this reinforces the feeling.

Back on the wards the last four weeks have gone very slowly but I have now received written confirmation that I have passed my final exams. I am now doubly qualified with both my Registered Mental Nursing (RMN) and my State Registered Nursing (SRN) qualifications. I have been back to see the matron of the general hospital to tell her my good news and she has again offered me the vacant charge nurse's post on the locked ground floor admission ward of the Professorial Department of Psychological Medicine. I am thrilled. I can hardly believe my good luck and of course I have accepted the offer.

I have put my notice in to Mr Gibbons the Chief Male Nurse and he has accepted it with good grace. I am due to start my new job in a month's time. For the first time in seven years I will be permanently in charge of a ward and I will be able to ensure that the patients under my care will not suffer any abuse or neglect. They will be treated exactly as I would wish to be treated with the best individual care and treatment that I and the staff can provide. As for any nurses I discover to be involved in abuse or neglect I will be down on to them like a ton of bricks. As far as I am concerned the time for standing by and doing nothing is well and truly over.

End